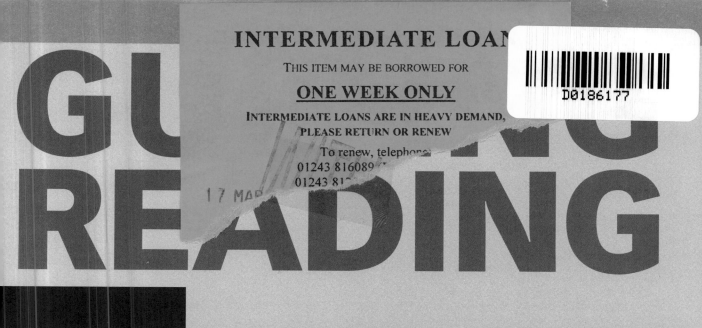

GUIDING READING

A handbook for teaching guided reading at Key Stage 2

Angela Hobsbaum, Nikki Gamble and David Reedy

First published 2002 by
The Institute of Education
University of London
20 Bedford Way
London WC1H 0AL

Reprinted with amendments 2002

British Library Cataloguing-in-Publication Data
A catalogue entry for this book is available from the British Library.

ISBN 0 85473 647 6

Designed by Peter Dolton
Production services by Book Production Consultants plc
25–27 High Street, Chesterton, Cambridge CB4 1ND
Printed in England by The Wolsey Press, Ipswich

CONTENTS

ACKNOWLEDGEMENTS

In writing this book, we have been generously supported by the National Literacy Strategy, whose help and critical feedback we gratefully appreciate. Louise Dempsey and Isabel Wright, from Nord Anglia Hackney, contributed Part 3 and we enjoyed their collaborative and constructive discussions. Many consultants recommended texts for inclusion in the lists; in particular we should like to thank Louise Dempsey, Sally Elborn and Melanie Ravenscroft for their extensive contributions. Two teachers, Norma Earle and Debra Maidman, generously made time to talk to us and allowed us to take photographs in their classrooms. Sabrina Antâo organised the lists and dealt with all copyright matters in her competent and wonderfully unflappable way. In the end, the errors and omissions are all ours.

PREFACE

When *Book Bands for Guided Reading* for Key Stage 1 was first published in 1998, it seemed to meet a need felt by many teachers for guidance with this new teaching approach. A second edition produced in 2000 was even more popular and we were constantly receiving requests to 'produce one for Key Stage 2'. Eventually the clamour became irresistible, and I thought the task might be an interesting, if challenging, enterprise. I was fortunate enough to be introduced to two experts who knew much more about children in Key Stage 2 than I did and together we started to discuss what a book on guided reading in Key Stage 2 should include and how teachers might be helped to develop their expertise.

It rapidly became clear to us that a gradient of text difficulty, which has been an important feature of the organisation of texts in Key Stage 1, would not work in Key Stage 2. What makes texts understandable to children who are reading at NC Level 2 and above is not simply a matter of the features of the text but is affected by the background knowledge, interests and motivation that the pupils bring to the reading task together with what they are being asked to do. This combination of internal factors together with the relation to the rest of the class work – what is being covered in maths, geography, history or science – and the specific reading task set, together make text difficulty something which, we felt, could not be stamped on a book. While there may be some general features of the text which affect its readability, these only provide broad guidelines. In order to make a successful match between children's reading abilities and a text, a teacher needs to know a great deal about the particular pupils' interests and histories as well as about texts.

As we grappled with the problem of how best to help teachers, the stream of requests for 'Book Bands for Key Stage 2' became a flood. When I've talked to callers, I've tried to explain why the book wouldn't be 'Book Bands for older readers'. I'm afraid that, if you want a simple way to organise your books, you will be disappointed. But if you can rise to the challenge of expanding your ideas about what guided reading really involves, we hope that you will find this book helpful and that your pupils will reap the benefits.

Angela Hobsbaum

PART 1

What is guided reading?

DIFFERENT WAYS OF TEACHING READING

The debate about how to teach reading has raged unprofitably for many years but more recent research has begun to achieve some consensus about what children need to be taught. Studies of classroom management have illuminated the effectiveness of different approaches to teaching reading. The National Literacy Strategy (DfEE, 1998) has built on this research to encourage teachers to use different ways of teaching reading. Before the National Literacy Strategy (NLS) was introduced, teachers' practice was often a mixture of what they had learned in college, what their school encouraged, and ideas they had gleaned from in-service courses. They frequently spent a lot of time hearing children read individually, a practice which has been criticised as inefficient by Ofsted (1996), time-consuming for the teacher and often unproductive for the children, who may merely be practising their skills. The Strategy presents three kinds of reading: shared reading, guided reading and independent reading, each requiring different kinds of teaching approaches and classroom organisation. These three models were first developed in New Zealand in the 1980s and each element has its own place in a unified literacy curriculum.

In **shared reading**, the teacher's role is to make overt what good readers do: modelling the process so that the children can follow her example. It's called shared reading because children and teachers can all see the text, by using a big book or overhead transparencies. Because the teacher is the reader, he or she can support the pupils to appreciate material that may be slightly harder than they can read on their own. Pupils can concentrate on the meaning without having to decode each word for themselves. The teacher acts as model, demonstrator and instructor, leading a discussion about the interpretation of the text. The pupils listen to the text read aloud, join in and follow the reading, and learn from the teacher's example of analysing the text. In the Literacy Hour, shared reading is followed by a detailed focus on relevant features at word, sentence or text level in which the teacher draws attention to key aspects, making links with previous material and encouraging the children to notice what's important.

In **guided reading**, the teacher is acting as the expert who guides the learners through the text, by providing signposts to the most important and most helpful features of the textual landscape. It follows from this analogy that the teacher must know the landscape well. Teachers must know not only the text but also the processes of learning that they have the responsibility to develop.

The view of the teacher as guide has recently been applied to many educational settings through interest in the work of Vygotsky and his concept of the scaffolding provided by an expert to help a novice to scale the heights (Wood, 1998). The scaffolding is a temporary structure that helps learners reach the next rung on the ladder; it will be unnecessary once they can achieve this without help. The goal of guided reading is to enable learners to become independent, able to read, understand and appreciate texts on their own without the teacher's help. To do this, the learners gradually internalise the teacher's prompts and cues so that the external support becomes part of their own system. At that point, when the teacher's support has become redundant, they have become independent readers. Providing guidance that is of most use to the learner is a skill: guidance needs to be matched closely to the learner's current level of achievement, which is why it can't be done in whole-class situations where the range of abilities will be too wide. In small groups the teacher can observe each child's behaviour closely to see the processes by which they are creating meaning from the text and then offer prompts to develop strategies which are within their learning zone.

In **independent reading** the child practises without the teacher's help. That practice will be at whatever level is appropriate; a lot of practice on the lower slopes is needed before you tackle the heights! In reading, practice is vital in order to build up automaticity. The component skills need to become so well practised that they no longer require conscious attention and the reader can concentrate instead on other features. It's like learning to drive: at first the learner is deliberately concentrating on pedals, gear lever and mirror; with practice these movements become automatic and the driver can focus on traffic conditions, road signs and the whole environment. The teacher has a vital role: to suggest the route the young reader takes, offering a variety of interesting materials and ensuring that the pupil has plenty of opportunity to consolidate reading skills on appropriate books. This too is an art, because matching the text to the reader is not just a technical process but one that requires a grasp of the reader's interests and prior knowledge as well as skills. Motivation for reading is critical; the teacher needs to ensure that each child's appetite for reading can be satisfied from the variety of books available.

As well as these three kinds of reading, the teacher also needs to make an opportunity to **read to** the class, not necessarily as part of the literacy hour. Reading to pupils can enable them to share the enjoyment of literature, extending their experience of the world through the book, finding out about new writers and whetting their appetites for reading. Being read to should be a shared pleasure rather than an opportunity for direct teaching. From stories on tape and *Go 4 It* to *Book at Bedtime*, hearing a story read aloud well can be a joy for a listener of any age. Sometimes a book that is being read to the class may become the focus of a guided reading session, but a book shouldn't be chosen because it can be used in this way. It must be chosen on its merits for each situation.

GUIDED READING IN THE NATIONAL LITERACY STRATEGY

In the *NLS Framework for teaching*, the learning objectives are organised into a progression of increasing complexity and the teacher's task is to present these objectives through texts that match the group's level of reading skill and mix of interests.

If the teacher is going to be a competent guide he or she needs to have different kinds of expert knowledge:
- knowledge about the subject matter: the features of text which convey shades of meaning
- knowledge of texts that offer good quality material suitable for teaching
- knowledge about the learner: how children develop, how reading develops and where each individual learner is in terms of their own progress along this developmental path, taking account of individual differences, interests, and the social context of the classroom and group
- the really specialist understanding which enables the teacher to combine all those spheres of knowledge in the practice of their craft: the pedagogic knowledge of how to teach.

Many teachers do this almost unconsciously and indeed expert practitioners may not consciously attend to this process for much of the time as they make skilful decisions about what to draw children's attention to or when to intervene. But teachers will benefit from thinking about what they do from time to time so that they can reflect upon what's happening, meet new challenges and articulate their practice in order to lead professional development. Just as a mountain guide will combine his familiarity with the terrain and his interpretation of the latest weather forecast with his judgement about the skill of his clients, so teachers must combine what they know about the challenges in a particular text and the requirements of the curriculum with what they think their particular class can tackle with confidence and enjoyment. Who'd entrust their safety to an ill-equipped mountain guide when they are planning an ascent of Everest? Teaching children to read well is just as challenging a journey: the goal is to make children readers not merely children who can read.

We have written this book to try to help Key Stage 2 teachers understand what is involved in guided reading because it requires so many skills to be brought together and has only recently been introduced systematically in England. It requires teachers to develop their practice in order to work effectively with small groups rather than with individuals, developing clearly focused tasks which can be completed in a limited time and which will extend the range of strategies children can use on their own. We have called it *Guiding Reading* to emphasise the importance of the teacher's role; it is what the teacher does that makes guided reading effective. By guiding their reading, the teacher is enhancing the pupils' reading strategies so that they will be able to internalise these approaches and apply them when reading independently. By reading with a guide, pupils will be able to read with more awareness and understanding and will bring these skills to bear when they tackle texts alone.

WHY USE GUIDED READING?

Teachers in the past thought that the best way to teach reading was by hearing children read. However, studies of what actually happens when children read to teachers (Wheldall *et al.*, 1992) show that what occurs is fairly repetitive: when children stumble over a word the teacher will wait, then give a clue and, if that fails, tell them the word. Occasionally this is accompanied by reference to a more general rule. The children are practising or rehearsing their reading, but is the teaching really helpful? Considerable time was devoted to hearing all the children in a class each week (Ireson *et al.*, 1995) and the same kind of strategies would be pointed out to many children, somewhat inefficiently, as the teacher repeatedly offered suggestions like 'look at the first letter; what does it start with?' 'Did you notice the punctuation there? How would that sound then?' or 'What do you think is going to happen next?' Hearing children read may be useful when assessing their reading skills but it is not a good way to teach reading.

In guided reading, the teacher has an explicit teaching role: to point out the relevant features of text and ensure that children have the strategies to cope with them. It is more efficient because, by grouping children at similar levels of achievement, the teacher can provide guidance that meets the needs of the whole group, rather than one by one. Also, by working together, children can learn from each other, discussing texts and putting their heads together to find information. Guided reading should be a more effective and efficient way of teaching as well as being enjoyable for the pupils.

WHAT DOES GUIDED READING LOOK LIKE IN KS2, AS CHILDREN BECOME MORE CAPABLE READERS?

Learning a cognitive skill is an invisible process; it goes on inside the learner's head. Sometimes the behaviour we see gives us a clue to what's going on between the ears. When young children in the early stages of reading say the words aloud, we can often infer the processes behind their behaviour and we can try to unravel their confusions. Even this process is tricky and we can't be sure that we are always right; sometimes when we think children are making guesses because of the appearance of a word, they may in fact have been more influenced by their expectation of the story or a glance at the picture. But once children cease to read aloud, the whole process of what's going on in their heads becomes harder to follow. How can teachers know how to help them?

Teachers need to find ways to explore children's learning in order to demonstrate different reading strategies that can be used. In Parts 3, 4 and 5, we offer examples of questions that teachers can ask, to extend pupils' thinking. By discussing the text in detail, teachers can unravel the process of children's developing understanding. As children become more skilful readers, they focus less on the mechanics of decoding and can appreciate more subtle features that deepen their understanding of the complexity of the text. At the beginning of Year 3, most pupils are becoming independent readers of text at an appropriate level, but they will still be reading largely for the content – for the story-line, the characters or the information. As pupils mature, the whole-class programme teaches them to read beneath the surface of the text and to consider other issues such as the author's intent, style and standpoint, and the effectiveness of different features in varied styles of writing. These reading skills then become a focus in guided reading sessions.

With their growing maturity, we want pupils to take increasing responsibility for their reading. This will include
- the selection (and rejection) of texts as they develop preferences which they can defend
- posing their own questions before, during and after reading
- making their own decisions about what aspects of the text they should consider in relation to a range of purposes for reading
- evaluating and reviewing texts and sharing their judgements with their peers and other people.

In order to talk about these processes, children need a vocabulary to describe the texts they read. It is the teacher's role to know how to refer to features of text using technical terms accurately and Part 5 of this book (pp. 137–76) provides a helpful introduction to this.

WHAT IS THE TEACHER'S ROLE AND HOW DOES IT CHANGE?

In Key Stage 1, as children are in the emergent and early stages of learning to read, the teacher's role is to provide texts which offer appropriate challenges in terms of learning the orthography (the writing system) and getting the meaning from text. Working with cues at word, sentence and text level, the teacher deliberately ensures that children understand not only how sounds make up words but also what those words mean and what the whole text is about. Close matching of the level of text difficulty to the children's reading level will enable children to practise and to devote attention to new words or structures while not losing sight of the meaning. Understanding, enjoying and appreciating the text is an integral part of reading;

comprehension is not an 'optional extra' to be added on after the text has been read. Using all the cues to get meaning from text will be an explicit part of teaching.

By Key Stage 2, as children become more fluent readers, their developing cognitive skills will enable them to grapple with the complexity of English morphology (the way words are built up), which will underpin their spelling as well as their ability to work out new word meanings as they grasp affixes, suffixes and roots. As the mechanical process of decoding requires less attention, children can become more analytic about the text itself and their response to it. Their growing metacognitive skills enable them to be more aware of their own reading strategies and more able to monitor their understanding. They will need to read texts for many different purposes as more of the curriculum will be text-based, from maths problems to science reports to history projects. They will need to read in different ways for different purposes.

Key Stage 2 is also an important phase of social as well as cognitive development. During these middle childhood years, children become more socially aware and interested in a range of issues beyond their immediate environment. They become concerned about fairness, justice and punishment; about motives and aspirations; about the environment and sustainability; and their understanding of these concepts develops from concrete to abstract. Their reading can play a role in this development, as they read to find out more, to understand the experience of others, and to establish their own views, opinions and tastes.

The teacher can harness children's growing social maturity by using techniques such as **reciprocal teaching** (Palincsar and Brown, 1986, 1988) by which strategies that children can use to explore a text are deliberately taught. The teacher models explicit ways of summarising, asking questions, clarifying and predicting and helps the group to practise them until they can use them independently. The responsibility for using the appropriate strategy is then shared with the pupils, who can take turns to lead the discussion. A useful video, *Reciprocal Teaching: Extending reading strategies,* demonstrating reciprocal teaching, can be obtained from Madeleine Lindley Ltd.[1]

USING THIS BOOK

Part 2 looks in more detail at the development of reading skills in Key Stage 2. Part 3 covers the planning and organisation of guided reading: what the teacher needs to do when preparing this part of the literacy hour. Part 4 provides exemplar lessons and lists of texts for each of the year groups. In Part 5, the key features of the main kinds of text – narrative, poetry and non-fiction – are described and linked to the *NLS Framework for teaching.* Part 6 suggests ways of using this book for professional development within a school. Finally, in Part 7, suggestions for further reading are included so that teachers who would like to learn more about reading processes or about particular genres or authors can follow up their interests in more depth. The NLS Illustrative Target Statements for reading are included as an Appendix for reference.

1 Madeleine Lindley Ltd, Book Centre, Broadgate, Broadway Business Park, Oldham, OL9 9XA. 0161-683-4400.

REFERENCES

DfEE (1998) *The National Literacy Strategy Framework for Teaching*. London: DfEE.

Ireson, J., Blatchford, P. and Joscelyne, T. (1995) 'What do teachers do? Classroom activities in the initial teaching of reading'. *Educational Psychology* 15: 245–56.

Ofsted (1996) *The Teaching of Reading in 45 Inner London Primary Schools.* London: Ofsted.

Palincsar, A.S. and Brown, A. (1986) 'Interactive teaching to promote independent learning from text'. *The Reading Teacher* 39(8): 771–7.

Palincsar, A.S. and Brown, A. (1988) 'Teaching and practicing thinking skills to promote comprehension in the context of group problem solving'. *Remedial and Special Education* 9(1): 53–9.

Wheldall, K., Colmar, S., Wenban-Smith, J., Morgan, A. and Quance, B. (1992) 'Teacher–child oral reading interactions: how do teachers typically tutor?' *Educational Psychology* 12: 177–94.

Wood, D. (1998) *How Children Think and Learn* (2nd edn). Oxford: Blackwell.

PART 2

The development of children as readers in Key Stage 2

relates to its meaning. They mark number, tense and manner and are generally unproblematic for the learner. However, plurals are not completely regular; the rule of adding -s changes to -es, depending on the final sound of the singular word. These irregularities don't cause problems for children when they read, since the word is likely to be familiar to them in all its forms. But they can be troublesome when they write, as they need to think about whether to add -s or -es. However, the sound of the word helps them, as -es endings sound different (e.g. *glasses* /iz/) from -s endings (*books* /s/). Here, knowing the grapheme–phoneme relations will solve the problem.

Tenses are also marked by morphemes and here the sound doesn't help the speller. While the past tense of *help*, *burn* and *wait* sound different (help/t/, burn/d/, wait/id/) they are all spelled the same. More confusingly, there are other words which sound like these verbs, such as *soft* or *bold*, which are not spelled using -ed. How is the learner to know what to do? If children follow their ears and represent /t/ with -t, they will make mistakes when writing *helped* (helpt) or *kissed* (kisst) although they'll get *slept* and *swept* right!

Children approach the complexities of written language in the same way that, as toddlers, they approached the task of learning to speak. Young children notice the regularities in the speech they hear, figure out a rule for themselves and then over-generalise it, saying 'hurted', 'falled' and 'goed' as well as *washed* and *climbed*. Gradually, by listening to others, they learn that there are different patterns. The speech they hear provides the input to their increasingly sophisticated processing system, while the role of adult teaching, whether modelling or correction, is less clear.

The same process can be seen as children learn to write. They have never read the forms 'kisst' or 'jumpt', but that's what their ears tell them to write. As they realise,

When children arrive at school they are already able to use oral language but few will be readers. During their school years, their language skills will develop to embrace literacy. However, oral and written language are not identical. We do not speak in sentences; we talk in utterances and oral language has its own conventions. Particular grammatical conventions that are applied to written language, such as that sentences have to start with a capital letter or that all sentences should have a verb, have to be learned in the context of written language. During the school years, the course of oral and written language development will diverge, with written language becoming less and less like everyday speech and the language children read and write becoming less and less like what they hear around them. Only in certain situations (e.g. giving feedback to the whole class, making a presentation in assembly, reading a play script aloud, delivering a speech, giving a lecture or taking part in a prepared debate) will oral and literate language coincide.

WHAT MAKES WRITTEN LANGUAGE HARD TO UNDERSTAND?

Written language differs from spoken language in a number of ways and since most people do not talk like books, children's acquaintance with the forms of written language will be mainly through what they hear read aloud to them (such as in shared reading sessions or when texts are read aloud, at home, at school or at church) and in what they come to be able to read for themselves. Speech is generally easy to follow because it takes place face to face, and may be accompanied by a range of gestures, expressions and intonation; even on the telephone when the listener can't see the speaker, they can ask for clarification: 'What did you say? I didn't catch that.' In written language every word may be important for the meaning to be grasped and punctuation is a poor substitute for expressive intonation.

from their reading, that past tenses are formed with -ed, they'll correct their mistakes, and write *kissed* and *jumped* but also 'sofed' and 'sleped'. The more instances of correct forms that they read, the more opportunities they have to infer the rules for themselves. While the evidence for this development may be seen in what children write, their growing understanding is fuelled by what they read. It is not clear why it takes so long for children to work out these grammatical rules but it is clear that this level of understanding is more complex than that required for mastery of phonological rules. Cognitive growth, which continues well into late childhood, will be affected by access to print.

DEEPENING UNDERSTANDING: BEING ABLE TO LOOK AT THE TEXT AS OBJECT

Courtney Cazden (1976) uses the analogy of language as a window: when children first learn to talk, they see through the transparent medium, quite unaware of its properties and thinking only about using it to communicate. When they go to school, however, teachers draw their attention to the characteristics of the medium itself by correcting their every mistake. We might make a similar comparison with children learning to read: at first they concentrate on the words and their meaning; the message is derived from the words in the text. Only later will they distinguish literal from figurative meaning, appreciate the features of the plot, note how the author has created suspense; make inferences; understand the double-entendre or pun; admire the illustrator's skill in conveying a special effect: all that is involved in seeing the text as an artificial construction.

This process of being able to look at the text as something to be appreciated, interrogated, explored and disputed can start early but will develop as the reader brings more experience of reading and of the world to each new text. The conscious awareness and monitoring of one's skills is also a later development. In the early stages of learning to read, the teacher tries to help the processes to become automatic so that the skills do not require conscious attention but roll off smoothly like the movements of an expert typist. But later it is important for the reader to develop the ability to become aware not of the sub-routines, but of the text as object and of one's understanding and response to it.

READING AT NC LEVEL 3 AND BEYOND

Once children are reading at NC Level 3 and beyond, the main focus for development is the move towards autonomy. As children become more independent readers, they will be establishing and consolidating positive attitudes to reading. Children should be encouraged to develop and discuss their reading preferences. As tastes in authors, illustrators and genres emerge, these need to be supported by well-informed teaching. An enthusiasm and love of literature is more likely to be developed by enthusiastic teachers who enjoy the pleasures of reading and appreciate the profound impact of good literature. Throughout Key Stage 2 children should be guided rather than pressured or coerced to develop reading habits in a way that promotes their autonomy.

READING STRATEGIES

At NC Level 3, readers are consolidating the alphabetic process in what Frith (1985) has termed the orthographic stage, where children become more efficient at translating print into pronunciation and can make use of their growing knowledge of spelling patterns and morphemic boundaries to read new words. The reading strategies that children have learnt to use in the earlier stages are integrated, sight vocabulary increases and, as these processes become automatic, the ability to reflect on reading processes develops.

At this stage readers are able to tackle a range of texts fluently and accurately but may still need support with more challenging material. By NC Level 4, confidence increases and readers are able to use a wide range of strategies automatically, though they may still sub-vocalise when reading particularly challenging material in, for example, an unfamiliar genre.

It is important that readers in these crucial stages continue to have opportunities to listen to experienced readers reading aloud and that they also have opportunities to read aloud to each other; for example, in pairs during a shared reading experience or during guided reading. Through listening to stories, poetry and reports read aloud they will continue to develop an ear for the rhythms and patterns of language in different genres. Working with complete texts ensures that holistic language learning takes place, in order that choices about sentence construction and vocabulary are understood in the context of the impact created and the effect on the reader.

Because readers in Year 3 will be using a range of strategies it is still necessary for the teacher to continue modelling reading strategies such as self-correction, reading-on, rereading, using prior knowledge about genre and content in order to encourage the development of reflective reading strategies. In shared and guided reading, discussion about vocabulary is important to avoid the potential problem of children becoming excellent decoders without understanding the meaning of words or the nuances of vocabulary.

Throughout Key Stage 2 children should be encouraged to talk about aspects of reading they find difficult and to develop strategies that help them to develop positive images of themselves as readers and to give the teacher greater insight into the nature of reading difficulty and challenge. Furthermore, in making these processes explicit, readers will come to have a better understanding of them.

DEVELOPMENT OF UNDERSTANDING: IMPLICIT MEANING AND INFERENCE

It is now generally accepted that meaning does not lie exclusively in the written text but in the interaction between author, text and reader. Louise Rosenblatt (1978) argues that when a reader encounters a text, the new meanings that are generated are greater than those intrinsic to the text or indeed the reader's previous understandings. Importantly in such transactional theories of reading, the reader is an active participant in the process of making meaning. And as readers' knowledge and prior experiences will vary, a text may offer multiple meanings. It is essential that teaching takes account of children's prior knowledge and experience and actively encourages them to discuss the personal significance of books read. While a book may offer unlimited personal responses, interpretation is to some extent limited by the possibilities offered from within the text and at NC Levels 4 and 5 readers can begin to appreciate the distinction between personal significance (what it means to the reader) and interpretation (what the author may have intended).

Genre will also affect interpretation and readers will adjust their responses to suit the type of text they are reading. Thus violence in a cartoon strip will not elicit the same response as violence in a serious autobiographical account, even if the context is similar. Strategic readers are reflective and will adjust their understandings in the light of knowledge about a text type.

Children working at NC Level 2 and above will be beginning to make inferences and deductions based on explicit and implicit information. At NC Level 3 they will, for example, infer character traits, cause and effect relationships, and will be able to use textual clues to predict outcomes. Increasingly at NC Levels 4 and 5 readers are able to justify the inferences they make, referring to the text to support their opinions. At NC Level 4 children are more able to understand abstract texts that are not obviously related to personal experiences and they can begin to make connections between passages in extended narrative, for example in looking at how a theme is developed in several key passages.

Book talk is essential for developing readers' understandings of the multi-layered meanings of texts. The key to good book talk is good questioning that does not inhibit response, but guides the reader to more considered understandings. Teachers who have not yet discovered Aidan Chambers' book (1993) *Tell Me* will find this practical book a delight. Chambers writes with a considerable depth of understanding about what constitutes purposeful book talk, avoiding what can appear to be the testing approach of some question and answer sessions.

For children working at NC Level 2 and above, shared and guided reading sessions provide the context for learning about different genres, developing book knowledge and increasing awareness of an author's style. Providing opportunities for children to read in cross-curricular contexts increases children's familiarity with the full range of genres in meaningful situations. It is far better to read an information book about the Tudors if this topic is being studied in history, or to read a range of recipes as procedural texts when working on a unit about food technology than to cover this work in isolation from the rest of the curriculum.

Providing plenty of opportunities for children to compare texts either across genres or within the same genre provides a framework to support analytical thinking. Picture books are still an essential component of the reading curriculum throughout Key Stage 2, offering complexity of themes, implied meanings and inter-textual references, and proving that an accessible text need not be an unchallenging one. An example of how picture books can be used in a challenging guided reading session is provided in Part 4 (pp. 126–9) and Part 5 includes information about the features of different kinds of text so that teachers can enhance pupils' appreciation.

Another benefit of reading is that children encounter many words which refer to mental and psychological states – words like *insist, imply, concede, infer, assume, assert, deny* – which are not used in speech because the speaker's actions carry the force of the intent. The speaker doesn't need to say 'I assert that ...' because the act of saying something emphatically *is* the assertion. By meeting these words in print, the reader learns to distinguish and appreciate a range of mental states, thereby increasing awareness of others' intentions.

RESPONSE TO LITERATURE

By selecting work of genuine literary quality, richer responses can be evoked. In responding to literature, readers develop an emotional response to the content of a text, develop empathy with the characters or make an aesthetic judgement about an author's use of imagery or language.

At NC Level 3 children can begin to make critical comparisons between texts and discuss the personal significance of a particular text. As children develop greater capacities to decentre to other viewpoints, they will be able to consider the possibilities of alternative readings and discuss the validity of these readings.

In developing children's appreciation of literature, learning in the affective and cognitive domains is simultaneously promoted. While younger children are more ready to respond emotionally, throughout Key Stage 2 readers can start to engage in more objective evaluation. Children will be able to make judgements about the elements of reality and fantasy present in a text, distinguish between fact and opinion and judge the validity of viewpoints. D.W. Harding wrote that '*responding to a great work means becoming something different from your previous self*'. And it is certainly important that children have opportunities to reflect on how their thoughts and feelings change in the light of their reading. At NC Level 5 and beyond, readers should have developed a mature approach to reading, being able to respond with emotional involvement while at the same time maintaining a reflective detachment. A still more sophisticated response is the readers' ability to use analogy from reading to enhance the significance of their own lives.

In identifying strategies that refine children's responses to the books they read, we need to develop ways of working which enhance their appreciation rather than relying on excessive questioning. A written response might include jottings in a reading notebook (see p. 29). Various drama strategies such as hot-seating characters can be employed to develop empathy. Sometimes children can be asked to make an initial response through drawing, painting or modelling. The different ways in which children choose to respond can be used as the stimulus for discussion that opens up the possibilities of meaning in text rather than closing them down.

ACCESSING INFORMATION: USING STUDY SKILLS

It is worth reminding ourselves that the distinction between this section and the previous one is not about the difference between reading fiction and non-fiction but about reading purposes. The criteria of literary quality can apply not only to fiction and poetry but to non-fiction books as well. For example, a good biography can evoke an empathic response and a well-written history can engage a child emotionally as well as increasing their factual knowledge. Furthermore, fiction and poetry can be used as sources of information. The novels of Charles Dickens, for instance, may set the context for studying social history of the nineteenth century.

At NC Level 3 children are able to use reference material, locating information through contents, indexes and glossaries. Throughout Key Stage 2 the development of independent learning should be encouraged as children use the skills taught in shared and guided reading for their own research purposes. NC Levels 4 and 5 are characterised by growing confidence in applying research skills and the ability to comment critically on information sources. Readers working at NC Level 5 will be able to find key material and reject irrelevant information. Mallet (1992) and Wray and Lewis (1997) offer frameworks for developing children's skills in this aspect of their reading. In Part 5, some key features of non-fiction texts are described.

FLEXIBLE READING STRATEGIES

Most of the books that children read for pleasure will be story books, where interest in the narrative will keep children reading to find out what happens. Non-fiction texts lack the structure of plot and characterisation to grip the reader's attention; they do not have a beginning, a climax and an end. Moreover, they are generally trying to teach the reader something new, so unfamiliarity with the subject matter is an additional handicap. Children need to be taught that reading non-fiction requires many different strategies that need to be applied flexibly, depending on the purpose for reading. These strategies need to be practised frequently if they are to be used effectively.

Contrasting fiction and non-fiction texts will highlight the obvious differences in layout and structure but readers need ample experience in using what Neate (1992) calls the 'structural guiders' in order to become proficient users of information books. It is hard to abandon the habit of starting at the front and reading through to the end. (Is that what you are doing here?) Using the index, the contents page or the glossary requires the ability to sift information and search for what is relevant – which is very difficult if you don't know exactly what you are searching for.

Reading non-fiction requires the reader to develop a detachment from the text that is quite different from the ability to be immersed in a story. The reader must scan for information and assess whether the information offered is adequate, accurate and appropriate for the purpose. The purpose may be to find the answer to a question posed by the teacher or by the child and it is often thought to be more motivating to encourage children to define their own questions. But some of the questions that children ask will not be profitable to pursue; Mallet (1992) lists questions like 'Where does the squirrel get its name?' and 'How many kinds of squirrels are there in the world?' as commonly asked questions, which don't really contribute to understanding these creatures. Neate (1992) suggests helping children to frame useful questions using *who? why? when? where? how?* and *what?* to produce questions like 'Why do cats have whiskers?', 'How do cats get whiskers?', 'What colour are cats' whiskers?' or 'Where do cats have whiskers?' All these might be answered through research. Understanding what makes a good question is the first skill that needs to be taught.

If the first step in reading an information book is to have a clear purpose such as a question to answer, the next is to be able to use the structural organisers to locate the relevant information. Having found, from the contents or the index, what seems to be an appropriate place, the reader needs to scan to see whether the reference is really helpful. All too often children will start with the first reference in the index and work through uncritically. Again, it takes practice to scan four references and decide which one is most informative for your purpose. Finally, the information must be read more closely to understand and evaluate it. If the task requires summarising, this may require making notes or highlighting key points. Working out whether material is comprehensible is a sophisticated metacognitive monitoring task, requiring the reader to analyse what they have read very carefully in relation to their existing knowledge.

Reciprocal teaching, mentioned in Part 1 (p. 6) offers one way of helping children read information texts actively. The teacher initially models clarification (**What does *erupt* mean?**); summarising (**What's this passage about? What's the main idea here?**); questioning (**What I'd like to know is …**) and prediction (**What might the**

writer tell us next?). As children become familiar with this structure, they can take over the role of questioner, and assume responsibility for leading the group through each paragraph of a non-fiction text. This technique can be incorporated into guided reading sessions.

DIVERSITY IN DEVELOPMENT

Every teacher will be aware of individual children's differences in reading development and achievement that affect their responses to print. Two groups of pupils who deserve particular attention are children with English as an additional language and those who are struggling to keep up, especially those who have not yet reached NC Level 2b.

Learners with EAL becoming English readers

It is widely assumed that learners with EAL need a certain level of proficiency in oral English before they begin to read English but there is less agreement about whether this is an essential or a desirable attribute and very little consensus about the level of oral proficiency required. But teachers in Key Stage 2 will have to start wherever the child is: a 10-year-old newcomer to England with very limited spoken English may have good awareness of the functions of print and have more advanced learning strategies to apply to the task of learning to read English than a younger child with better oral fluency. Cummins (1984, Cummins and Swain, 1986) has argued persuasively that children's proficiency in their second language will be enhanced by their ability to transfer relevant skills and strategies from their first to their second language. However, many learners with EAL in Britain are not taught literacy in their first language in a school context, although within their community they may be taught to read and write in their home or heritage language. The literacy-learning settings and expectations will differ widely and indeed the concept and purpose of literacy may also differ in different settings. Some learners with EAL may think the early stage of learning to read means rote-learning a text, rather than interpreting and enjoying it, as is likely to be stressed in British classrooms.

Their limited proficiency in spoken English means that they will have poorer knowledge of acceptable sound patterns and weaker skills at predicting syntactic structures. This means that questions like 'Does it sound right?' may not be helpful because their ears are less attuned to what 'sounds right' in English. They are more likely to rely on decoding strategies that may also be emphasised as the appropriate way to learn to read in their first language. But grapheme–phoneme irregularities will cause them problems, and as their vocabulary is limited, they will find it hard to choose the right match for the words they decode – so 'mi-shap' (like *bishop*) and 'un-ite' (like *unwell*) will sound acceptable, as will 'rowboat' as a pronunciation for *robot*.

Studies have shown that young bilinguals are more advanced in detecting rhymes and segmenting sounds in words, suggesting that early bilingual experience may improve their phonological awareness. But the problems of different cultural expectations and experiences may outweigh these advantages. Children with EAL learning to read English frequently have to learn to read about things which are unfamiliar, in a language which is also unfamiliar. No wonder they struggle! Guided reading can provide a particularly supportive context for them. Activating prior knowledge – through looking at the pictures or discussing the plot in advance or reminding the children about relevant background knowledge and terminology – is critical for learners with EAL. The difficulty of a reading task is a function of both the difficulty of the text and the difficulty of the content. So, if the content can be made accessible by using texts which are culturally appropriate or which draw on shared first-hand experience, such as a science experiment or some practical work, the reader has more cognitive capacity to attend to the reading task itself. Texts, both fiction and non-fiction, where the illustrations are particularly supportive, will be helpful to the reader with EAL for whom this contextual scaffolding is vital.

Many children with EAL will be developing their knowledge of English, especially syntactic structures and vocabulary, through their reading, so reading becomes the engine for their oral skills rather than the other way round. While content words are easy to learn through reading, function words are always harder to learn and particular care needs to be taken to ensure that these unobtrusive little words are properly understood. Words such as *until, unless, however, furthermore* carry a weight of meaning yet are hard to comprehend. Children with EAL will also need explicit instruction in syntactic structures that are new or unfamiliar. The benefit of guided reading is that the teacher can adapt the teaching more sensitively to fit these pupils' learning zone.

While some writers suggest that children need a culturally-responsive pedagogy – an approach to teaching which is sensitive to their cultural expectations – in many British classrooms there is such a diversity of cultures that this is unattainable. It may be feasible in essentially bilingual settings where there are also bilingual teachers who understand the cultural and linguistic background of the pupils with EAL, but in most British classrooms the teacher is monolingual and may have children from many cultural and linguistic backgrounds in her class.

Children reading below NC Level 2b

Although the focus of this book is on children who are already reading at an age-appropriate level, throughout Key Stage 2 there will be some children who cannot do this. Their problems may be due to many causes and it is not helpful here to discuss issues of differential diagnosis. What is important is to try to ensure that the text they are offered matches as closely as possible their reading level, since reading at frustration level (making more than one error every ten words) is unlikely to be an enjoyable or motivating experience. However, the older children get, the harder it will become to find texts which match their interest and their reading level appropriately. Hence the importance of getting them under way with reading as quickly as possible! *Book Bands for Guided Reading* (Bickler *et al.*, 2000) describes a range of books organised in terms of the difficulty of the text, but these will generally appeal to younger readers. Short books that children can read at one session are more motivating than long books. Books that capitalise on children's interest in sports, hobbies, pets, pop stars – where the content is familiar and relevant – may be useful. Picture books which don't look too babyish, such as cartoon books on serious themes like Raymond Briggs' *When the Wind Blows*, may be helpful. The example of a guided reading session based on a picture book in Year 6 (pp. 126–9) shows how an accessible text can provide worthwhile learning opportunities for older pupils. Simplified texts, which aim to combine more mature interests with less challenging text difficulty, may be useful but need to be selected carefully.

Reading mileage
It is vital for children in Key Stage 2 who are still reading at or below NC Level 2 to read as much as they possibly can. Reading enhances vocabulary learning and the more practice children have on texts that support their emerging strategies, the better they

become. Studies have shown that the gap between the better and the weaker readers widens dramatically; in one American first-grade class, a study found that a child in the lowest group read 16 words in a week while a child in the highest group read nearly 2,000! Even the average reader was already reading three times as much text as the weakest and these differences became more pronounced over time. Reading is the most effective way to learn new vocabulary, because talk tends to use common words, while books have less frequent, more specialised vocabulary. Vocabulary knowledge enhances understanding and general knowledge, so the more children read, the more new words they will encounter and the more their comprehension will improve. Surveys in the USA show that children do not read much out of school; they spend more time watching television than reading, so the encouragement of reading in school is especially crucial. The amount of time spent reading books – and thus exposure to print – makes a significant difference to vocabulary knowledge. Using Teaching Assistants or volunteers to engage these children with books may be a good investment.

Reading aloud

Children who are not yet fluent readers will benefit considerably from hearing text read aloud, whether fiction or non-fiction. As there are fewer opportunities to hear information books read aloud, this may be even more helpful in enabling them to access less common vocabulary and structures and concept-dense text. Reading aloud more challenging texts will support these students and enhance their confidence to tackle difficult material.

Keep expectations high

It is important to have high expectations for all children and not to confuse easy tasks with easy texts. Devising challenging tasks around less difficult texts may be tricky but it will ensure that these children are given tasks at an appropriate cognitive level. Commercially produced simplified texts are not always easier to understand because short sentences from which connectives have been stripped away may be harder to follow than longer ones (see Part 5, non-fiction texts p. 162).

Emphasise fluency

Reading poetry or plays may be a good way to encourage less fluent readers to read faster and with more expression. Slow reading hinders comprehension because the start of the sentence has been forgotten before the end is reached. Patterns which are close to oral language or are predictable and supportive can encourage faster processing.

Silent reading

Silent reading is faster than reading aloud so pupils should be able to understand material better when they read silently than when they read aloud, especially if their oral reading is halting. Discussion to encourage them to explore interpretations and ensure that they have grasped the meaning is a good way to help them to appreciate texts.

All children are different and those who are slow to get off to a good start may be a particularly diverse group. While guided reading provides an ideal opportunity to address their particular needs, it is important to ensure that at other times they have the chance to work with more capable readers.

REFERENCES

Bickler, S., Baker, S., Hobsbaum, A., Prance, J. and Douëtil, J. (2000) *Book Bands for Guided Reading: Organising Key Stage One texts for the Literacy Hour*. London: Institute of Education, University of London.

Briggs, R. (1984) *When the Wind Blows.* London: Hamish Hamilton.

Cazden, C. (1976) 'How knowledge about language helps the classroom teacher – or does it? A personal account', *Urban Review* 9: 74–91.

Chambers, A. (1993) *Tell Me.* Stroud, Gloucestershire: Thimble Press.

Cummins, J. (1984) *Bilingualism and Special Education: Issues in Assessment and Pedagogy*. Clevedon: Multilingual Matters.

Cummins, J. and Swain, M. (1986) *Bilingualism in Education: Aspects of theory, research and practice*. Harlow: Longman.

Frith, U. (1985) 'Beneath the surface of developmental dyslexia' in K.E. Patterson, J.C. Marshall and M. Coltheart (eds) *Surface Dyslexia: Neuropsychological and cognitive studies of phonological reading*. Hove: Lawrence Erlbaum Associates.

Mallett, M. (1992) *Making Facts Matter: Reading non-fiction 5–11*. London: Paul Chapman.

Neate, B. (1992) *Finding Out About Finding Out*. Sevenoaks: Hodder and Stoughton/UKRA.

Perera, K. (1984) *Children's Writing and Reading*. Oxford: Blackwell.

Rosenblatt, L. (1978) *The Reader, the Text, the Poem: The transactional theory of the literary work*. Carbondale: Southern Illinois University Press.

Wray, D. and Lewis, M. (1997) *Extending Literacy: Children reading and writing non-fiction.* London: Routledge.

PART 3

Planning and organising guided reading for children in Key Stage 2

Louise Dempsey and Isabel Wright

Guided reading is an approach to teaching reading that supports pupils' development as active and independent readers.

It is most effective when:
- it works within a balanced reading and writing programme
- pupils are actively engaged in the reading process and can discuss their reading with others, guided by the teacher
- pupils are encouraged to apply their new learning independently within a range of contexts (independent/paired reading of the guided text; rereading known texts; exploring texts by the same author/same text type, etc.).

This part of the book explores the process of teaching guided reading. It includes two case studies (pp. 30–2, 32–4), which demonstrate the decisions made by two class teachers in order to run successful guided reading programmes in Year 4 and Year 6, and concludes by addressing a number of common questions about the practical implementation of guided reading.

The purpose of this part is not to dictate a formula for the teaching of guided reading. It aims to present the key decisions and steps that teachers need to work through and to share some possible models.

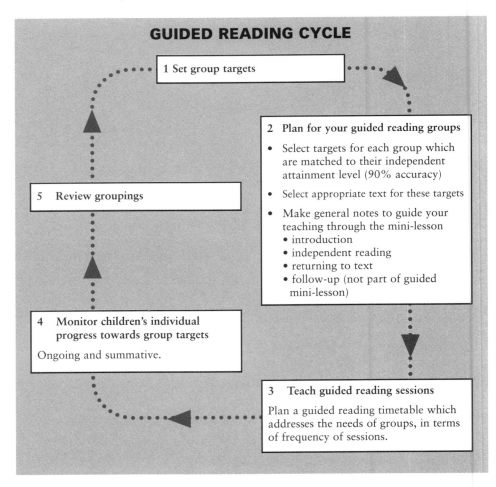

GUIDED READING CYCLE

1 Set group targets

2 Plan for your guided reading groups
- Select targets for each group which are matched to their independent attainment level (90% accuracy)
- Select appropriate text for these targets
- Make general notes to guide your teaching through the mini-lesson
  - introduction
  - independent reading
  - returning to text
  - follow-up (not part of guided mini-lesson)

5 Review groupings

4 Monitor children's individual progress towards group targets
Ongoing and summative.

3 Teach guided reading sessions
Plan a guided reading timetable which addresses the needs of groups, in terms of frequency of sessions.

STARTING POINT

What levels are the pupils currently attaining in reading? What strategies can they currently apply independently and what do they need next?

The teaching in a guided reading session aims to build on what pupils know and can do already, and to develop their ability to apply new strategies independently. Therefore, teachers need to have a clear idea of:

- pupils' current levels of attainment;
- the specific reading skills and strategies that, if developed, would enhance pupils' ability to read, to understand and to reflect on what they are reading.

What pupils can do will, to a large extent, reflect what they have been taught. In the earlier stages of learning to read, much of the teaching is to do with learning to use specific strategies, the orchestration of reading cues, and expecting reading to make sense. However, once pupils are reading at NC Level 3, the emphasis moves to the higher order skills of developing a deeper understanding of the text through use of inference, deduction and evaluation (NC Level 3 and 4 Level Descriptors, National Curriculum for English). This means that we need to establish what aspects of the specific level descriptors pupils can currently apply independently, and then make choices about which of the remaining aspects to tackle next.

There is no single correct order in which to work through the aspects of a particular level descriptor. For example, with a group which can currently 'read a range of texts fluently and accurately' (NC Level 3), the teacher could choose to tackle 'identifying and articulating the main points' or 'expressing preferences' next, depending on which aspect is judged to be most useful and on the current focus of the class programme. This process is most powerful when the pupils are involved in self-evaluation and identification of the next steps. When this happens, pupils become more committed to their own learning, in addition to gaining the skills they will need as independent learners.

On-going guided reading records, supported by teacher observations and other assessment and record-keeping systems, are the best source of the knowledge needed to make useful decisions about particular groupings of pupils. It is important to draw on the observations and records of all the adults who work with the pupils on reading and also on pupils' self- and peer-assessment.

The section on questions (p. 27) indicates how teachers can explore children's developing understanding of texts. The section on assessment (pp. 35–8) shows a range of formative and summative assessment tools that have been successfully used by class teachers to record progress, assess levels and inform decisions about groupings. They also support decisions about what the pupils need to focus on next.

The Illustrative Target Statements for reading (in the Appendix, pp. 197–209) provide a cumulative description of the development of reading behaviours from Reception to Year 6 and can be used to inform planning and as an aid to monitoring achievement at class or school level.

WHAT ARE THE KEY COMPONENTS OF A GUIDED READING SESSION?

The structure of the guided reading session, promoted by the NLS and described below, creates a clear structure for both pupils and teachers. However, as demonstrated in both the case studies and some of the exemplar lesson plans (for example, Guided Reading Year 3, Stories by the same author, pp. 54–5), guided reading sessions can be approached in a variety of ways. Teachers' decisions to vary the structure will depend on the nature of the text, the group's level and the specific targets being addressed.

Text introduction

The purpose of the introduction is to orientate the readers to the text and to focus them on the particular purpose of the guided reading session. With a new text the focus of the book introduction could include:

- references to other known books by the same author or of the same genre or text-type;
- an introduction to the content, style and vocabulary of the text; this could be achieved by reading the 'blurb', a section of the text, using the teacher's prior knowledge of the text, and/or the pupils' predictions and expectations of the text;
- references to other related experiences and learning across the curriculum.

With an on-going text (started either in previous guided or independent reading sessions, in another curriculum area or through whole-class reading), the book introduction could include:

- discussion about the part of the book the group has already read;
- predictions about the rest of the book;
- discussion about content, vocabulary, style, authorial intent, purpose and audience, pupils' views and opinions.

> **THE STRUCTURE OF GUIDED READING SESSIONS**
>
> In guided reading, the aim is to support pupils to apply key targets and strategies whilst reading independently. Over time pupils need opportunities within guided reading sessions to:
> - activate prior knowledge
> - make predictions
> - remember and explore their targets and strategies
> - read independently, bringing to bear their prior knowledge, predictions and key targets and strategies
> - discuss what they have read
> - reflect on reading and review progress made during the session.

In either case, the focus for the text introduction will be determined by the teacher's judgement on how much there is a need to support and consolidate pupils' understanding of the content and by the particular targets identified for the group to develop.

> Later in this section (pp. 27–8), we discuss the use of questions and prompts that can generate in-depth discussion between pupils and enable the teacher gradually to hand over the management of the whole reading session to the group. Teachers need to curb the dominance of their role during guided reading sessions. As part of this process, it is important for teachers to ensure that they achieve a balance between facilitating discussion and participating as a member of the group.

Strategy check

Following the text introduction, pupils should be asked to recall the full range of strategies which they know and aim to apply as they read to ensure maximum understanding of the text and an explicit focus on their reading targets.

For pupils reading at NC Level 3, this involves using the full range of phonic, graphic, semantic and contextual cue-sources to achieve fluent reading. As pupils move towards NC Level 4, these will be combined with more sophisticated strategies, such as making links across and between texts, visualisation, asking questions, making and checking predictions based on inference and deduction as well as on the information given directly. The group will be encouraged to apply those strategies that are most useful in relation to the particular targets they are currently working on.

For example, a group whose targets include the use of inference to read beneath the surface of the text, would be prompted to:

- connect information across the text;
- discuss the impact of particular connectives on the information that follows them;
- verbalise what is shown about a character through her/his actions rather than what is told directly to the reader.

A group whose targets include identification of authorial intent would be prompted to:

- identify the purpose and audience of a piece of persuasive writing;
- identify the use of words and phrases that exaggerate to persuade;
- evaluate the effectiveness of the piece in persuading the intended reader.

Independent reading

During this part of the session, pupils read the next section of the text with a particular focus on the targets and strategies already discussed. Depending on what these are, it may be appropriate for pupils to:

- read individually or in pairs;
- reread a section for deeper meaning or read on;
- skim for the overall message;
- scan for specific information;
- read closely for a deeper understanding.

Much of the independent reading of longer texts – particularly with more fluent readers – may take place as an independent or paired activity, in the Literacy Hour, at another part of the day and/or as homework. It may be that discussion, with reference to the text, forms the major focus of some guided sessions.

However, it is important to continue to hear pupils read sections of the text out loud, in order to monitor accuracy, phrasing, fluency and comprehension, and to prompt pupils to interact with the text during, rather than after, reading. Active readers absorb meaning from text in a range of ways. They may visualise, hear the text aloud in their head, ask questions, make connections and think ahead, hold thoughts whilst they read on, and speculate and predict. Active readers select from this range according to the purpose of the reading and the demands of the text. Once these strategies have been modelled (during shared reading and again as part of the strategy check) and practised by the pupils, teachers can use the independent section of guided reading sessions to prompt pupils to apply these strategies as appropriate.

Returning to the text

This section of the guided reading session has a number of functions. It is an opportunity to:

- identify any points that need clarification, exemplification and/or discussion;
- revisit the key targets and strategies and draw on examples of their application. These examples will often arise when the teacher is listening to individuals as they read out loud or will be noticed by the pupils themselves in their own reading;
- review a particular comprehension strategy. For example, pupils may have been asked to visualise as they read, with the objective of noticing the impact of the setting on the atmosphere of a story or piece of travel writing. This would lead to a discussion of what they 'saw', and whether or not it enabled them to arrive at a fuller understanding of the text they have read.

Over time, the responsibility for facilitating discussion should transfer from the teacher to the pupils. Individual pupils could take on the role of leading the review, in relation to specific targets and key strategies and facilitating discussion between their peers. In order to achieve this, the teacher needs to model explicitly how to lead the 'review', and to stage a gradual hand-over of responsibility to the pupils. Reciprocal teaching, discussed in Part 2 (pp. 16–17) is one way of achieving this.

Response to the text

Once the reading strategies have been applied to achieve full comprehension, the group can discuss their responses to the text, supporting their arguments with reference to the text where appropriate. Being able to explain preferences and articulate reasons will encourage a genuine dialogue and a view of the self as a reader.

WHAT ARE THE CRITERIA FOR SELECTING QUALITY TEXTS FOR GUIDED READING?

It is crucial that the teacher should choose not only quality texts but also texts that offer useful opportunities to work towards specific targets. In part 4 we include lists of books for each year group after the appropriate exemplars. In addition, the QCA document *Target Setting and Assessment in the NLS* provides a list of fiction and non-fiction 'benchmark' books. These serve to exemplify the appropriate reading level for each year group, and can be used to establish comparable reading levels for other texts. For pupils working below NC Level 3, *Book Bands for Guided Reading: Organising Key Stage One texts for the Literacy Hour* (Bickler *et al.*, 2000) offers detailed guidance on text selection, and extensive lists of books at each level.

Most publishers now produce levelled guided reading texts, some of which offer teachers' notes on delivering guided reading and on the content, style and text features of the books.

Basic guiding principles

Texts for guided reading should be selected for the quality of the content, use of language and attractive presentation. The goal is for pupils to develop as independent readers of sophisticated texts for a range of purposes, which include both study and recreation. To achieve this, they need to encounter engaging, well-written and well-presented texts, reflecting the full range of fiction and non-fiction text types. Reading (fiction and non-fiction) offers the opportunity to learn about life both as we know it and beyond our immediate experience. It is essential, therefore, that pupils' reading both reflects their direct experience and offers them opportunities to experience and understand the world through the eyes of others. This includes reading texts with positive role models in relation to race, religion, gender, family structures, sexuality and disability. Guided reading provides the opportunity to model how to be a discerning reader and how to find and appreciate quality texts.

Texts for guided reading should match the reading level of the group. In terms of reading fluency, pupils should be able to read the text at between 90 to 94 per cent accuracy, and with understanding. However, for pupils in Key Stage 2 who are reading at or above NC Level 3, reading goes far beyond the decoding of words and it is important to consider the balance of familiar and new in relation to knowledge of the content, language style and structures, cultural references and organisation when considering the level of a text. In general, learners can only focus on what is new and challenging within a context where enough is known to enable them to orchestrate the cue-sources of context, syntax, graphics and phonics.

Where possible, texts should match the range being taught to the whole class, or which relate to another area of current learning or interest. This will mean that pupils will learn to apply their targets and strategies on texts which they have authentic reasons to read.

The text must offer opportunities to apply the targets and strategies that form the group's current focus. For example, when trying to extend NC Level 3 pupils' ability to use inference, it is important to select texts that don't make everything explicit. Many texts written for children who are just beginning to read longer texts independently do not require pupils to read beyond the information given.

GETTING TO KNOW THE TEXTS

In order to teach guided reading effectively at NC Levels 3 and 4 it is important to know the texts to be used. Being thoroughly familiar with at least the relevant section will ensure that the teacher is able to generate focused discussion and that the text is appropriate for the purpose of the session.

QUESTIONS, PROMPTS AND STATEMENTS

One of the most powerful components of guided reading is focused discussion about the text, in relation to specific targets. This is generated through the use of questions and prompts.

Questions, prompts and statements should encourage pupils to explore their ideas and opinions and to evaluate both the texts and themselves as readers.

Questions

It is essential that pupils reading at NC Level 3 and above move beyond simple comprehension and recall questions and consider questions that require them to:

- **Deduce**: draw conclusions from the information given throughout the text;

- **Infer**: read between the lines to draw tentative conclusions which are based on but go beyond the information given in the text;

- **Justify** their responses by referring to the text itself;

- **Evaluate**: make critical judgements relating to the text, about the author's effectiveness and their own responses.

Quality discussion, in which pupils apply these skills, supports their development as sophisticated and independent readers. A further development would be to work with pupils on devising appropriate questions for themselves and each other, in relation to their group target.

> **Question categories and examples**
>
> **Literal questions:** repeating directly, or in own words what the text says
>
> Can you tell me what happened when/who/where? What are the main points in this non-fiction text?
>
> **Inferential questions:**
>
> Will ___ stay or leave and what makes you think this?
>
> **Deductive questions:**
>
> Explain … using two or more points to justify this.
>
> **Asking for justification:**
>
> Where does it imply that? What in the text makes you say that?
>
> **Evaluative questions:**
>
> Is this a successful piece of persuasive writing? Why/why not?
>
> Does this passage succeed in creating suspense? Why/why not?

Prompts and statements

In guided reading sessions with more fluent readers, it is important to move beyond teacher-led discussion. Real discussions do not generally revolve around one person's questions. Instead, they involve people in:

- making tentative statements to see what they think about something
- changing their minds
- listening to others' views and responses
- formulating considered responses through verbalising, refining and asking their own questions.

Discussion during guided reading sessions is a powerful opportunity to model and develop these skills. Teachers should be vigilant about the dominance of their role during the discussion and view themselves as participants rather than as leaders. Four useful ways to facilitate discussion are to:

- **wait** before offering statements, prompts or even very tentative thinking, to give pupils an opportunity to voice their ideas first
- **listen** carefully to what pupils say
- **support** and encourage pupils to ask their own questions and to lead the discussion
- **use paired talk** as a strategy to offer pupils thinking time and time to formulate quality answers before contributing to the group discussion.

> **STATEMENTS/PROMPTS:**
> - The text has made me feel angry
> - I wonder why …
> - Some people say that …
> - It reminds me of …
> - I can't remember where we first learnt about ___'s feelings.
> - I still don't think I know enough about …
> - I'm not sure what I think about…

DEVELOPING PUPILS' RESPONSES TO TEXTS

The main aim of any reading programme which goes beyond teaching pupils to decode is to deepen and extend pupils' responses to text. This will serve them both in their future studies and in any reading they choose to do beyond education. By developing pupils' responses to text, it is more likely that they will continue to study successfully and will choose to read, both for work and for pleasure.

Active readers seek answers as they read. They may not consciously pose themselves questions, but the desire to make sense and to reflect are prime motivators in any active reading. In guided reading sessions, teachers and pupils can make this process explicit through posing questions before, during and after reading. This is particularly important with more challenging texts. When pupils are actively seeking to learn something specific, they need to sift through challenging information, selecting and rejecting it in relation to their questions. When pupils read without a specific purpose, they are more likely to give up and lose interest.

Questions play an important role in developing pupils' ability to interact with the text. Inferential, deductive, justifying and evaluative questions (see p. 27) help pupils to engage with the text and to go beyond the literal meaning. While pupils are reading a fiction text, teachers may ask questions such as:

- How do you know that?
- Can you show me the part of the text that tells us that?
- How did the author create the effect you have just described?
- Why do you think the author chose to do what you have just described?

Questions prompt pupils to explain, express and justify their opinions and to evaluate the text and their own responses to it. The goal is for pupils to internalise the process of asking themselves questions of this nature as they read so that they become active readers. A step towards this is for them to pose questions to each other during guided and independent reading.

**READING
NOTEBOOKS**

Another powerful mechanism for developing deeper responses to texts is the reading notebook. The aim is not to produce a record of what each pupil has read. Rather, it is to provide a place where pupils can note their questions, thoughts, predictions, responses and evaluations before, during or after reading. For many pupils (and teachers) the maxim *how do I know what I think until I see what I have written?* is worth reflecting on. Reading notebooks give pupils an opportunity for recording tentative thinking during reading that can then feed into an evaluation after reading. As such, they are useful for teacher–pupil and pupil–pupil dialogue and can feed into the group discussion. They also offer one method of formative assessment. Because one of the key purposes of reading notebooks is to allow pupils to communicate with themselves, their peers and with the teacher, it is important to agree some ground rules on their use and the extent to which teachers have access to them. It is not always necessary for teachers to read them, but, if they do, they should respond primarily to the content. If pupils are to be encouraged to risk recording their tentative thinking, they need to feel confident that it is their thoughts that will be responded to and not their secretarial skills. This is not to say that no attention should be paid to spelling and handwriting. Any conversation about these aspects should focus on how more fluent spelling and clearer handwriting would make it easier for pupils both to write in and to read their own notebooks.

It can also be productive if, at times, the teacher keeps a reading notebook and addresses some of the same questions and issues as the pupils are considering. This both models the process to the pupils, and produces an equality within a group of readers, which enables the teacher and pupils to learn together.

CASE STUDIES

This section is designed to demonstrate the practicalities of planning and teaching guided reading. It presents some of the decisions made by a Year 4 and a Year 6 teacher in order to plan and teach guided reading successfully.

CASE STUDY YEAR 4

Norma Earle teaches a Year 4 class at Lauriston School in Hackney. She has 32 pupils, of whom 17 are girls. Twelve pupils are on the SEN register and three pupils have statements. Seven pupils have English as an Additional Language and are stage 2 and 3 learners (Hilary Hester language fluency levels).

The pupils fall into five attainment groups for reading:
  Groups A and B: 14 pupils NC level 3/4
  Group C: 6 pupils NC level 3B
  Group D: 6 pupils NC level 2A
  Group E: 6 pupils NC level 1A

Norma groups her pupils via a range of formative and summative assessments. These include:
- QCA optional tests
- Teacher-designed reading comprehension tests, to assess what has been taught, which includes layered (levelled) questions
- Interviews with pupils
- Teacher observations during guided reading
- Individual reading sessions with pupils.

The groups are fluid and reflect progress and pupils' needs.

> Johan is an excellent reader and has good comprehension, but he feels insecure in a group. He attends two guided reading sessions, one at the appropriate level and one with the group one level below. This was his decision and has had an impact on his confidence as a reader.

> Lilia has made significant progress this term and is ready to move to the next group. As a transition, she is attending both the new higher attainment group and her current group.

Norma works closely with her Teaching Assistant (TA), who supports two pupils with statements in the lower attainment group. They plan together every week to ensure a clear focus on the group's needs and links to the class programme. The TA runs a supported reading session with the lower attainment group every day and supports the pupils with planned activities that are linked to the class programme and differentiated for the group.

Norma teaches guided reading during the Literacy Hour and teaches additional groups during a daily reading session. The school also prioritises an additional writing session each week.

Norma usually alternates guided reading and writing each week. However, she will alter this cycle if particular blocks of work lend themselves to either reading or writing.

During the additional daily reading, a range of reading activities takes place:
- Reading to groups/the class
- Guided reading
- Individual reading/reflecting sessions with the teacher
- Shared reading
- Personal reading
- Paired reading
- Sharing and reviewing texts
- Supported reading (TA)

In Norma's class she makes links between the whole-class objectives and group targets. For each block of work, Norma identifies the key reading objectives. These objectives are then differentiated for the different groups. Guided reading therefore offers the pupils an opportunity to apply learning objectives to independent level texts.

Once again, when selecting texts, Norma endeavours to make links to the genre which is the focus of the whole class programme. She believes that this gives the pupils exposure to a range of texts in each genre, and an opportunity to reinforce and apply learning that has taken place during whole-class teaching.

The school has a central resource area for guided and shared reading material. Guided books at KS1 are levelled according to Book Bands and a similar colour-coding system is used for NC levels 3–5. The resource room includes a range of texts from different publishers. Norma also uses text extracts and real pieces of writing (newspaper and magazine reports, mail, etc.).

Norma uses group cards to indicate to groups the tasks to be completed, where pupils are working and which group is working with the teacher.

A literacy planning and assessment book is used to record the focus of the group session, key prompts and questions and notes about the pupils' progress during the session.

Norma uses a range of strategies when teaching guided reading.

For the lower attainment groups, she generally follows a generic structure which mirrors the NLS mini-lesson sequence. A real emphasis is placed on sharing the objectives for the session with the pupils and showing them what that looks like in relation to reading.

With the higher attainment groups, Norma varies the structure of the session. Some of the strategies she uses include:
- Posing questions before reading
- Paired discussion
- Pupils asking questions
- Pupils leading session/discussion
- Short bursts of reading (1 or 2 paragraphs) followed by discussion
- Seeking answers.

With all groups, Norma is very aware of the need to use both closed and open questions and the value of offering a statement or prompt to the group, instead of questions. She has high expectations about the responses she expects from the pupils and asks follow-up questions or prompts to extend answers and to encourage pupils to justify their views. She also expects pupils to make connections and use appropriate terminology.

Norma has a small classroom with limited storage space. She stores her teaching resources for the week in a central space. She places the books for the guided reading session on the table before each session. The classroom has a very small library area and the pupils keep reading material in their trays.

Norma records group tasks on a sheet of paper and fixes it with blu-tak to the laminated group card. These cards are then placed on the tables. The pupils are taught a series of steps to follow if they are unsure about the task:
1. Ask your literacy partner
2. Ask someone at your table
3. Ask someone from the next group
4. Ask the teacher

CASE STUDY YEAR 6

Debra Maidman teaches at William Bellamy Junior School in Barking and Dagenham.

There are 25 pupils in Debra's class, 11 boys and 14 girls. There are 2 pupils on the SEN register, and 1 pupil with a statement. There are no children in the early stages of developing English as an additional language.

The pupils are grouped into five reading groups:
    Group A: NC level 4: 6 pupils
    Group B: NC level 4: 6 pupils

Group C: NC level 3: 5 pupils
Group D: NC level 3: 6 pupils
Group E: NC level 2b/c: 2 pupils

Debra groups pupils using the results from the QCA optional tests and the Salford Reading test, to gain information about pupils' current attainment in reading. In addition she uses teacher observations during reading sessions to inform her judgements. Groupings are reviewed regularly and pupils move groups as appropriate.

William Bellamy Junior School made a decision to devote additional time to reading in order to raise levels of attainment in reading.

> We wanted to have quality teaching time with all groups every week.

A clear structure is established in Debra's class:

Guided reading takes place during our half-hour additional reading session, not during the Literacy Hour. During the week there is a clear routine. Each group engages with three structured reading activities and two independent/personal reading sessions linked to their guided reading text. One session prepares pupils for the guided session. It involves the pupils reading specific sections/ chapters and asking and answering questions. The next session is the guided reading session and the third session involves the pupils working independently and writing responses to questions and the text in their reading logs. In the other two sessions during the week children can read their own personal book, in silence.

Debra identifies long-term targets for her groups based on their current needs.

> The focus of the guided sessions with my top groups is currently on developing personal responses. My middle groups are working on identifying evidence in the text, looking closely at the text and giving reasons and opinions. There is also a focus on developing and understanding vocabulary. The lowest attainment group still needs to develop independent reading strategies, developing and orchestrating the searchlights.

At William Bellamy School the Year 6 teachers have each taken a few quality texts and planned a series of guided reading sessions. This means that they are building up a bank of exemplar guided reading plans and sharing good practice.

Sets of texts for guided reading in Year 6 are kept in the classroom. These sets include a range of fiction and non-fiction and represent a range of authors and publishers.

The guided sessions in Debra's class build on the preparation session the pupils have completed and prepare pupils for the follow-up session. There is an emphasis in the guided session on discussion, asking and answering questions and independent reading observed and developed by the teacher.

At William Bellamy Junior School, teachers record comments about pupils' progress on a guided reading record.

Debra feels that the additional guided reading sessions have had a significant impact on pupils' attainment and attitude to reading:

> Children really enjoy it. I know the children as readers much more than I did when I used to listen to them read independently. You can really deal with issues when you work within a group. It means that you can use formative assessment to plan for the following week much more easily.

Kevin Reading *Aquila* by Andrew Noriss:

> It's an adventure story, I like adventure stories. We've been working on this book for four weeks – mostly it's O.K. We've talked about the personalities of the boys and the description of the teachers. I like guided reading because you get to know how other people think. It is good to read it all together.

Charlie Reading *But You Promised* by Bel Mooney:

> We do guided reading on Wednesdays. We always have some questions to answer about our guided reading book. I like guided reading because we get involved in reading together. You can help each other when reading together by the answers you say. My favourite book this year has been a guided reading book, *The Butterfly Lion* by Michael Morpurgo, because I like sad stories and it was a bit sad.

HOW WILL I KNOW THE PUPILS HAVE MADE PROGRESS?

The teacher's role within guided reading is to prompt pupils towards independence in applying the strategies so as to meet the agreed target objectives for the session. This involves a combination of:

- Making pupils aware of the objectives and strategies which will have already been demonstrated and shared through whole-class shared reading;
- Encouraging pupils to problem-solve independently when they are in any way stuck;
- Feeding back to pupils on the effective application of target strategies and objectives;
- Using the group to problem-solve more intransigent problems.

During guided reading sessions, the teacher will keep a record of significant observations in relation to pupils' progress.

Formative assessment: collecting evidence

In contrast to the monitoring of writing, teachers don't automatically have any recorded evidence of pupils' progress in reading unless they note their observations. In order to be able to evaluate progress over time, and to make informed decisions about pupils' next steps, it is important that teachers keep regular records of pupils' reading behaviours and attainment during guided reading sessions. These records should be kept to the minimum, by only noting observations of significant behaviours and progress in relation to the group's guided reading targets.

Guided Reading Plan	Group Targets/Objectives 1. Blend common vowel phonemes; distinguish long/short vowels. 2. Recognise exclamation marks! 3. Discuss reasons for events in stories	Texts: .. Three Billy goats Gruff (play) Frog & Toad. Prince Cinders	Half Term: Autumn Term (2) 2000 Teacher/s Angela H. Level: 2C
Lesson Sequence			
1. Introduction:	Look at cover/title/blurb - what kind of book? Look at a few tricky words. Model blending and consider long/short vowels. Break sentences and look for exclamation marks		
2. Independent Reading:	Encourage reading with expression esp: with ! Prompt use of context to predict words and to decide.		
3. Returning to text:	Model what to do when make error - encourage ch'n to explain strategies. Ask children to identify events in story and why it was important.		
4. Follow Up:	DART on following day - add exclamation marks, or comprehension.		

Names and any individual targets	READING: Strategies, expression, fluency etc* Date and sign	RESPONSE TO TEXT: comprehension, opinion, reference to text (inference) * date and sign	Evaluation, next steps
Joe	Reading with more expression, but needs prompts for some punct.	Contributes enthusiastically; gives opinions, not always able to justify.	Good progress on all targets.
Kate	Able to correct errors; good grasp of word-construction. Becoming more fluent.	Keen to contribute; gives reasons for events although limited to literal.	Good progress on targets 1,2 need more on 3.
Sam	Sometimes still questions at words. Expression improving.	Reluctant to contribute; needs more support; shows understanding of text.	Needs more work on 3 but 1 & 2 improving.
Heather	Becoming more fluent but lacks expression with self-correct when reminded.	Can locate info in text but needs prompting to offer opinion.	More work on target 3. Needs also 2.
Charlie	Reads at slow pace but is starting to use expression & understanding of text & punctuation.	Is beginning to offer reasons to support opinions.	Making good progress on all targets; needs work on 2,3.

Whilst the pupils are reading (close reading, skimming, scanning, etc.), a key role for the teacher is to observe how the pupils problem-solve, and to use these observations to inform immediate and longer-term teaching decisions. Agreed group targets for the session provide the focus for the observations and, in general, any recording of pupil progress should be done in relation to these targets. Guided reading sessions provide teachers with an opportunity to observe pupils solving problems on their own, which is the closest teachers can get to seeing how pupils problem-solve when reading completely independently. This helps the teacher to ensure that any prompts and support offered are geared towards supporting the pupils' effective independent problem-solving strategies, and steering them away from strategies that hinder them.

Example

Group target: To 'scan' indexes, directories and IT sources, etc. to locate information accurately and quickly. (Year 3, term 3, T17)

A pupil in the Year 3 group tends to begin by scanning for key words, but then slips into close reading from the first one s/he finds, rather than continuing to find other examples and then deciding which is the best place to find the required information.

Prompts: What did you do when you found the first key word? (Carried on reading from there.)
How do you know that is the best place to start your close reading? Is there something else you need to do first? (Scan for other instances of the key word/s before starting close reading.)

Summative assessment

Formative assessment, which takes place during and after guided reading sessions, builds up a picture of pupils' progress over time. Summative assessment provides the opportunity for teachers to review progress made and identify future targets for pupils. At Key Stage 2, this may include interviews with or self-evaluations by pupils. They can then become actively involved in identifying the appropriate next steps for themselves as readers and can evaluate their progress towards these targets.

There are a number of possible assessments which may support existing school assessment procedures. Any system of assessment should be manageable and provide teachers with a clear picture of the progress pupils have made, their current attainment level, and the identification of next steps and groupings. For example, each child's progress in reading can be recorded in relation to aspects of the level descriptors.

Literacy Audit Section 1: Standards of Attainment

| Sheet 9 | Individual Record of Progress: **Reading** *NC Level 2A-5* |

Purpose: to evaluate individual progress in relation to level descriptors.

NB: This sheet can be used over a period of time (e.g. one year or a Key Stage) by colour coding different entries.

	Colour Coding	Date
School: Woodhill Primary **Child's name:** Ray O **Date of Birth:** 04.10.1992 **Gender:** Male **EAL:** Stage 4 **SEN:** **Starting date at current school:** Sept 1997		2.04.01 16.07.01

L2A:
Pupils read simple unfamiliar texts accurately. Their independent reading shows they can read ahead and make use of expression and intonation to enhance meaning. In responding to stories, they identify and comment on the main characters and how they relate to one another. They express opinions about events and actions and comment on some of the ways in which the text is written or presented.

L3
Pupils read a range of texts fluently and accurately. They read independently, using strategies appropriately to establish meaning. In responding to fiction and non-fiction they show understanding of the main points and express preferences. They use their knowledge of the alphabet to locate books and find information.

L4
In responding to a range of texts, pupils show understanding of significant idea, themes, events and characters, beginning to use inference and deduction. They refer to the text when explaining their views. They locate and use ideas and information.

L5
Pupils show understanding of a range of texts, selecting essential points and using inference and deduction where appropriate. In their responses, they identify key features, themes and characters and select sentences, phases and relevant

Comments (sign and date):

2.04.01: Ray's reading in more fluent and accurate. He is cross checking and self-correcting independently. His responses are limited to recapping the main points in a text.

16.07.01: Ray is able to give preferences and opinions and evaluate texts, however when the texts are more demanding he needs a lot of prompting.

A useful document offering practical guidance on setting short-, medium- and long-term targets and on establishing systems for keeping manageable records that have a clear purpose is *Target Setting and Assessment in the NLS: Book 1: Guidance on setting learning targets and assessing pupils' progress* (QCA, 1999).

The second booklet in this pack, *Book 2: Children's Work Exemplifying the Learning Targets and Suggested Criteria and Texts for Independence* (QCA, 1999), offers a range of exemplar reading and writing assessments. These include:

- reading interviews
- running records
- written activities which reveal what pupils have understood from their reading and their ability to apply knowledge and skills.

However, we know that there is a discrepancy between pupils' reading levels and what they can do in writing. Therefore we need to be cautious when setting writing tasks to measure reading progress.

Name	Gender	Age at test	Inf	Ret	Aut	Int	The	Feat	Totals Read	Totals Spell	Standardised Scores Read	Standardised Scores Spell	Levels Read	Levels Spell	Levels Write
Johnny	Boy	9.06	7	1	1	4	1	1	15	12	97	112	Level 3B	Level 3	just L3
Cassandra	Girl	10.04	10	2	5	8	2	5	32	15	116	116	Level 4A	Level 4	just L4
Sanjeet	Girl	10.00	12	1	2	10	1	2	28	14	112	115	Level 4B	Level 4	high L3
Steven	Boy	10.03	1		1	2		1	5	6	78	93	below L3	Level 3	Level 2A
Binh	Boy	10.02	7	2	3	9	2	3	26	11	108	105	Level 4C	Level 3	secure L3
Angela	Girl	9.07	2		1	5		1	9	7	88	99	below L3	Level 3	just L3
Rodney	Boy	10.09	8	2	1	8	2	1	22	10	98	100	Level 3A	Level 3	high L3
Ciaran	Boy	9.08	3			3			6	4	83	91	below L3	below L3	Level 2A
Julie	Girl	9.10	1	2	2	8	2	2	17	10	98	105	Level 3B	Level 3	just L3
Louise	Girl	9.06	5		2	2		2	11	9	92	104	below L3	Level 3	just L3
Hakim	Boy	10.07	7	2	1	7	2	1	20	9	97	99	Level 3A	Level 3	high L3
Harun	Girl	10.05	3	1	3	4	1	3	15	11	92	104	Level 3B	Level 3	secure L3
Samir	Boy	10.09	6	1	2	4	1	2	16	13	91	107	Level 3B	Level 3	Level 2B
Bianca	Girl	9.06	2			3			5	4	81	91	below L3	below L3	Level 2B
Adetole	Boy	10.02	4		2	3		2	11	6	88	94	below L3	Level 3	Level 2B
Karim	Boy	10.00	5		3	4		3	15	9	94	101	Level 3B	Level 3	high L3
Laura	Girl	9.08	5	1		6	1		13	10	94	106	Level 3C	Level 3	Level 2B
Sarah	Girl	9.08	6		1	5		1	13	8	94	101	Level 3C	Level 3	Level 2A
Ben	Boy	10.02	3	1	2	6	1	2	15	9	93	101	Level 3B	Level 3	Level 2B
Hayley	Girl	9.11	6		1	4		1	12	10	91	104	Level 3C	Level 3	just L3
Daniel	Boy	9.08	2	1	1	6	1	1	12	12	92	111	Level 3C	Level 3	secure L3
Christina	Girl	10.06	8		3	5		3	19	15	96	115	Level 3A	Level 4	secure L3
Abbie	Girl	10.04	3		2	5		2	12	12	88	107	Level 3C	Level 3	high L3
Matthew	Boy	9.09	7	1	2	4	1	2	17	9	99	103	Level 3B	Level 3	Level 2A
Jonathan	Boy	10.03	3	1	2	6	1	2	15	8	93	98	Level 3B	Level 3	just L3
Emma	Girl	9.10	4		1	5		1	11	10	90	105	below L3	Level 3	Level 2A
Jennie	Girl	10.04	7	1	2	7	1	2	20	11	98	104	Level 3A	Level 3	just L3
Rebecca	Girl	9.10	5	1	2	5	1	2	16	12	96	110	Level 3B	Level 3	just L3
Carlos	Boy	9.11	5		2	4		2	13	10	92	104	Level 3C	Level 3	Level 2A

Total Boys	14
Total Girls	15
Total Pupils	29

% Questions correct B	G	All		
59	32	56	Inf	Inference
54	43	51	Ret	Retrieval
53	21	45	Aut	Author's choice
61	42	58	Int	Interpretation
60	29	72	Them	Themes
60	27	57	Feat	Features of text

Teacher Name: The Oracle

Class: 5

If the QCA optional tests are used (see grid on p. 37), children's results can be entered into a spreadsheet that helps teachers to analyse the strengths of the class and areas of need in relation to specific aspects of reading.

Grouping pupils

Ideally, pupils should be grouped according to their current attainment and their identified next steps. For example, one group might include pupils who are reading at NC Level 3, who can read accurately and establish superficial meaning but are not able to give preferences and opinions and locate evidence in the text. With such a group, the teacher would use *the NLS Framework for teaching* to identify key objectives (e.g. Year 3, term 1, T8; or Year 4, term 3, T1) and choose one of them. The objective chosen then determines the focus for the teaching and supports the pupils towards independence.

This is the ideal model and it should normally be possible to group the majority of pupils in the class. However, grouping becomes more problematic if there are some pupils working at lower and higher levels within the class, or in classes which have an unusual spread of attainment. The overall aim should always be to balance what is possible with what the pupils need. It may be necessary to set up more flexible and fluid groupings to achieve this. For example, there may be two pupils reading at a level below the lowest group. The teacher may need to spend additional time with them as a pair to prepare and consolidate reading they are doing within their guided group.

It is important to remember that the NLS recommends that pupils only need to be in attainment groups for their guided reading and writing sessions. They should work in a range of groupings (pairs, mixed attainment, individually) for other reading experiences. This will enable them to have access to a full range of role models and to develop more collaborative learning strategies.

EFFECTIVE USE OF ADDITIONAL ADULTS

Many class teachers will have the support of an additional adult during literacy sessions or at other times of the day. Specialised teachers have a key role to play in teaching guided reading sessions to targeted groups. If additional teachers are involved in planning and evaluating pupil progress, they can offer very powerful reading experiences which are closely linked to group targets and reinforce the teaching and learning that has taken place during other sessions. It may be particularly helpful to use their expertise with pupils with EAL.

Teaching Assistants can also have an impact on children's reading attainment. Once again, with careful planning they can support groups of pupils or individuals with reading activities. This could be a supported reading session or preparing pupils for guided reading.

To prepare Teaching Assistants to work at this level requires careful training and joint planning. An effective way to achieve this is through observations of teacher-led guided reading sessions, with ample opportunities for discussion to emphasise the significance of group targets, the articulation of prompts and questions and agreed methods of record-keeping. Well-trained Teaching Assistants may also be able to provide additional time with EAL pupils who need extra support.

HOW MUCH TIME IS AVAILABLE FOR GUIDED READING?

This will very much depend on school arrangements and priorities. Some schools have identified additional time for guided reading outside the Literacy Hour, which allows more focused time for teachers and TAs to work intensively with groups, developing reading strategies. The two teachers in the case studies show different ways of organising their reading timetables.

NLS guidance recommends that pupils who are reading texts at the early levels (approximately *Book Bands* levels 1–5) need to be taught reading regularly (twice a week) for short sessions. Pupils reading at these early levels are usually in Key Stage 1. As pupils become more fluent readers, they need longer sessions of guided reading in order to allow time for more in-depth reading and discussion. At Key Stage 2, it is important to move towards a balance of guided reading and writing sessions, in order to develop and consolidate writing skills and to make the links between reading and writing.

The number and frequency of guided reading sessions for any particular group will need to be decided within the context of the overall literacy programme and the most effective way of meeting the needs of all pupils. This will vary from class to class and from school to school.

CONCLUSION

In order to organise a successful guided reading programme, teachers need to plan:
- groupings based on children's current attainments
- objectives based on appropriate reading targets
- teaching strategies to help children towards those objectives
- texts which will provide plenty of good learning opportunities
- ways of observing and assessing children's progress.

In the next part of the book there are examples of guided reading sessions that illustrate some of these key features.

REFERENCES

Bickler, S., Baker, S., Hobsbaum, A., Prance, J. and Douëtil, J. (2000) *Book Bands for Guided Reading: Organising Key Stage One texts for the Literacy Hour*. London: Institute of Education, University of London.

QCA (1999) *Target Setting and Assessment in the National Literacy Strategy*. London: Qualifications and Curriculum Authority.

The exemplar guided reading sessions: Years 3–6

GUIDED READING

YEARS 3–6

INTRODUCTION

This is the heart of the book. The following exemplar guided reading sessions are designed to be practical examples of how guided reading works in Key Stage 2 classrooms. All have been delivered successfully.

Our intention here is to give examples of guided reading using a wide range of texts with every year group. Each year group contains a fiction, non-fiction and poetry example as a minimum. In addition, in each year group there is one exemplar designated as more challenging. In these exemplars we have outlined how particular texts can be used with the highest achieving children.

We hope that these examples will be sufficiently clear for teachers to be able to use other texts in this way. The principles and structure that underpin them should be transparent enough to be applied to other examples from the range of books available.

YEAR AND TEXT TYPE

Every exemplar starts by stating the year group and the type of text (e.g. humorous poem) for which the lesson is designed. These categories are drawn from the range specified for the year group in *The National Literacy Strategy Framework for teaching*.

TEXT DETAILS

The title, author (if known), publisher, ISBN and source (if appropriate) are stated.

TEACHING OBJECTIVES

Every guided reading opportunity has to be based on targeting the teaching objectives that are relevant to a specific group of pupils. This enables the teaching to meet the needs of pupils at all stages of learning to read.

The teaching objectives that provide the focus of the exemplars are all drawn from the *NLS Framework for teaching* for the relevant year group.

As you read through the exemplars from Year 3 to Year 6 you will note that the teaching objectives progress in various ways. There is a particular focus on:

- fluent and accurate use of word level strategies;
- sustained silent reading;
- developing a broader repertoire of the ways in which one responds to literary and non-literary texts;
- developing personal responses and preferences.

TEXT SELECTION NOTES

It is important to specify why particular texts have been chosen as the basis for guided reading. The text selection notes explain why this text is judged to be worth using and the characteristics it contains which relate to the teaching objectives.

This section also includes background information about the texts that teachers need to know if they are to utilise them effectively.

LINK TO WHOLE-CLASS WORK

The exemplars may be linked explicitly to on-going work in the whole class during previous, concurrent or future Literacy Hours.

THE STRUCTURE OF THE GUIDED READING SESSIONS

This is where the exemplars move into what actually happens in the guided reading session.

TEXT INTRODUCTION

Many of the guided reading exemplars focus on a text introduction. This will include one or more of the following elements:

Text orientation: What kind of text is this? What expectations do I have before I read it? What information do I get from the front or back cover?

Pupils are expected to develop self-orientation strategies as they move through Key Stage 2 (see Year 4: Persuasive Texts, pp. 62–3):

* by making connections between the text and other texts they have read previously which may be related e.g. other work by the same author or of the same genre or text type;
* by making connections between the text and work or knowledge in other curriculum areas.

STRATEGY CHECK

Pupils and teachers together recall the range of reading strategies that will support their reading of this text type, stressing those that enhance comprehension. The teacher explains or reminds pupils about strategies included in the teaching objectives for the session so that it is clear to the pupils what they are about to do.

The teacher then tells the group what they are to do or think about while they are reading independently.

INDEPENDENT READING

Pupils read individually and independently within the group. As they move through Key Stage 2, this will increasingly be silent reading. This phase may extend over a number of sessions and could take place between guided reading sessions or as homework rather than within them (see Year 6: *Tom's Midnight Garden*, pp. 111–119). The following guided reading session will then focus almost exclusively upon returning to and responding to the text (i.e. will be a discussion session).

During independent reading it is important for the teacher to continue to intervene while pupils read. There is still an important place for the teacher to continue to hear children read short sections of the text out loud to monitor their reading accuracy, phrasing and fluency as well as comprehension.

Teachers may also intervene to support pupils in other ways, such as when they encounter difficulties with the meaning of specific vocabulary.

RETURNING TO THE TEXT

After the independent reading, the group goes back to the text to identify elements that may need to be clarified or discussed. The key element here is to review the application of the reading strategy that formed the teaching focus. This could be done through self-reflection by the pupils, prompted by the teacher, for example:

What do you now know about ... ?

What do you think you have learnt as a result of these three guided reading sessions?

Are you happy with what you have learnt? If not, why not?

This enables pupils to articulate their new knowledge.

RESPONSE TO THE TEXT

In this part we try to outline how, through questioning and discussion, teachers and pupils can establish an authentic dialogue around the text. This involves the teacher and pupils probing each other, extending comprehension and building personal preferences and responses.

As pupils move through Key Stage 2 this becomes increasingly important and thus the time allocated to it within guided reading sessions will increase correspondingly.

LINK TO INDEPENDENT WORK/ FURTHER READING

In many of the exemplars the guided reading extends over more than one session. Therefore, in this section we specify what children need to do independently in order to follow up the previous session as well as to prepare for the next one.

NOTE

There are four key points that need to be highlighted here.

1 **Not all the above elements need to occur in every guided reading session.** For example, in many exemplars the independent reading takes place between rather than within the session, so that the majority of time is spent on returning and responding to the text.

If a single text is being utilised over a number of sessions the text introduction will only take place in the first and not the subsequent sessions. With an on-going text (started either in previous guided or independent reading sessions, in another curriculum area or through whole-class reading), the book introduction could include:

- discussion about the part of the book the group has already read
- predictions about the rest of the book
- discussion about content, vocabulary, style, authorial intent, purpose and audience, pupils' views and opinions.

2 **The texts exemplified can be utilised in different ways to focus on other teaching objectives, or the same teaching objectives can be delivered in different ways using the same texts.** The ways the texts are used to teach here are not exclusive. A range of teaching objectives could be delivered by any of them and the activities and questions presented here are not the only way that the same teaching objectives could be delivered.

3 **Occasionally a text used during shared reading can also be used for guided reading.** This can take place at three points:

- Before being used for shared reading a group of pupils may consider the text and then, for example, present a book orientation to the class as a whole.
- Following shared reading, or between shared reading sessions based around the same text, a guided reading group might consider a part of the text in much more detail. For example a class may be reading 'The Highwayman' by Alfred Noyes. A guided group who need to work on how metaphor is used to create meaning may then focus on the first two stanzas of the poem in more depth.
- After shared reading, a guided group go over part of the text again. For example a higher-achieving group in Year 6 might spend more time on *Tom's Midnight Garden*

investigating further the author's manipulation of time and the links to the development of the relationship between the main characters.

Using a text which has been worked on during shared reading is not likely to occur on a regular basis because the shared text should be at a challenging level for the class as a whole. It would probably not be an appropriate text to support the targeted objectives for the majority of pupils in the class.

4 Whole texts rather than text extracts have been used wherever possible.
Text extracts, particularly those drawn from fiction and poetry, are not part of a process that ensures that the whole text is being read, which means that pupils are not being asked to respond as rounded readers. The text extract leads to an artificial reading experience and is then discarded. Pupils need to apply the teaching to the rest of the text, thus deepening their understanding as well as enjoying and responding to the text as a whole. Pupils need the chance to read whole texts as much as possible.

THE LISTS OF TEXTS

The lists are intended to be general indications of where particular texts could be used for guided reading. We have tried to group them so that there is an increase in challenge, in terms of theme, content and vocabulary as well as length.

Within the Year 3 list there are many texts that can be used with pupils who have achieved a solid level NC Level 2B in reading, as well as those who are already operating within NC Level 3. The crucial consideration for teachers when selecting which books to use is not that the texts are in themselves more challenging but that what we ask children to do with them is more challenging and that our selected teaching objectives provide the focus for the learning.

Teaching with picture books that contain few words can still challenge able readers even at the top end of Key Stage 2 (see the example in Year 6 based around the picture books *The Tunnel* by Anthony Browne and *Beware Beware* by Susan Hill and Angela Barrett, pp. 126–9).

However, we have also included a short section in each year group which is entitled 'More challenging'. This section is intended as a guide to some more difficult texts that could be suitable for the most experienced and capable readers in the year group – those operating two years or more beyond their peers. These texts are challenging in their content and subject matter, as well as the vocabulary they use. While some of the poems may be short, the fiction texts are often challenging in terms of the reading stamina that pupils will need to read them.

The lists are divided into three simple categories: fiction, non-fiction and poetry. In addition we have added some examples of other resources which teachers and literacy consultants have used to successfully deliver effective reading sessions. These include ICT resources, web sites, newspapers and magazines.

Selection criteria

The texts in the lists have been selected using the following criteria:

- They have all been used successfully in Guided Reading sessions in Key Stage 2 by the authors, or recommended by literacy consultants or Key Stage 2 teachers.

- We have not drawn heavily on books from educational publishers or reading schemes. Although many educational publishers are producing high quality guided reading books aimed at Key Stage 2 pupils, we felt it would be more valuable to identify texts that we know have worked well and that teachers would be familiar with and perhaps already have available in their schools, rather than simply list products that claim to be for guided reading. That said, a number of books from reading schemes are included in the lists where they have been recommended to us.

We need your help

Book lists in publications such as this one cannot be definitive. There are teachers in every school who will be saying 'They haven't included my all-time most effective title for Year 6!' New books will be published which will be eminently suitable for guided reading within Key Stage 2.

We want to hear from **you**. If you have a title (or titles) you think should be added to the lists please e-mail it to David Reedy (davidreedy@bardaglea.org.uk) so that it can be included in future editions or updates.

YEAR 3 EXEMPLAR GUIDED READING SESSIONS

GUIDED READING

YEAR 3

ADVENTURE STORY

COMPUTER GAMES
Gene Kemp

In *The Family Who Won A Million and Other Family Stories*

Compiled by Alison Sage

Red Fox (1997)

ISBN 0099668718

TEACHING OBJECTIVES

- To discuss characters' (i) feelings; (ii) behaviour, e.g. fair or unreasonable, brave or foolish; (iii) relationships, referring to the text and making judgements.
- To use awareness of grammar to decipher new or unfamiliar words e.g. to predict from the text, read on, leave a gap and reread; to use these strategies in conjunction with knowledge of phonemes, word recognition, graphic knowledge and context when reading.

TEXT SELECTION NOTES

'Computer Games' is a short story written by Gene Kemp, an author well known for her novels for children, particularly *The Turbulent Term of Tyke Tiler* and its sequels.

'Computer Games' is an adventure story, as the plot involves a boy becoming sucked into the game that he plays on his computer. In addition the story deals with the warp and weft of the relationship between two brothers, which Year 3 pupils are likely to be able to relate to their own relationships with siblings.

This family setting and theme are engaged with in the following example, which focuses on the relationships between characters as well as developing reading 'searchlights' as described by the NLS in the *Framework for teaching* (1998).

TEXT INTRODUCTION

- Pupils consider front cover of anthology and discuss what the stories will have in common and what 'compiled' means.
- Group then looks at beginning of story 'Computer Games'.
- Teacher explains teaching objectives. For example,

> This story is about two brothers. While you are reading it, think about the behaviour of the characters and how they feel about each other.

STRATEGY CHECK

Teacher explains how to orchestrate all the 'reading searchlights' when problem-solving on the text:

> You will be also working on using grammar to work out words which we are not sure about – this will involve reading to the end of the sentence and then going back. Look at the sentence on line 9 [*We're* supposed *to share it*]. I've written this on a piece of card and covered up the second word. Let's read the rest of the sentence. What words might fit? Let's have a look at the first syllable – which one of our ideas is right? Let's see the whole word. You can see how we used grammar by reading to the end of the sentence and phonic cues by sounding out the syllables to read the word correctly. Well done. When I listen to you read in turn I'll be listening and helping you to do the same thing on words you don't know.

INDEPENDENT READING

- The teacher tells pupils to read to the end of the fourth page. The teacher directs their attention to the main characters by asking the children to do the following:

> Think of words that describe each of the two boys. How do you think Adam feels about Tony? What makes you think this?

- During reading the teacher observes, prompts and praises. The teacher listens in particular to how pupils are using grammar cues in conjunction with the other searchlights.

RETURNING TO THE TEXT

- The teacher works with the group on specific teaching points, reinforcing the use of the reading strategy, for example:

> I was really impressed by the way you used the technique of reading to the end of the next sentence and then going back and reading the word at the end of the previous one using that as a clue. Can you show the others what you did?

- The teacher then prompts discussion around characterisation:

> How does Adam feel about his brother? What words might he use to describe his brother? What does it say in the story to make you think that? What's your evidence?

RESPONDING TO THE TEXT/LINK TO INDEPENDENT WORK/ FURTHER READING

The teacher asks pupils to read to the end of the story independently and then, when they have finished reading, to consider and then note in their reading notebooks:

> Will the way Tony treats Adam change as a result of his adventure? Why do you think that?

GUIDED READING

YEAR 3

TRADITIONAL TALE

THE PAPER BAG PRINCESS
Robert M. Munsch

Hippo Books (1980)

ISBN 0590711261

TEACHING OBJECTIVES

- To identify typical story themes, e.g. trials and forfeits, good over evil, weak over strong, wise over foolish.
- To infer the meaning of unknown words from context and generate a range of possible meanings.

TEXT SELECTION NOTES

The Paper Bag Princess, written by Robert M. Munsch, plays around with the stereotypical traditional tale themes and plot details. There are a Prince, a Princess and a dragon that needs to be defeated, but the beautiful Princess Elizabeth is the one who sets off in pursuit of the dragon after it has abducted Prince Ronald.

This is a short book which can be read quickly, but it is a funny and sophisticated story.

Children usually have strong views on whether this subversion of the genre works, or is even strictly necessary, thus leading to thoughtful and lively discussion.

LINK TO WHOLE-CLASS WORK

This guided reading session is most productive if it follows whole-class work on traditional tales and their features. The class will have looked at areas such as heroes and heroines, villains, magical creatures, problems and rewards, good over evil, recurring characters, etc. and therefore will have a conceptual framework within which to consider how *The Paper Bag Princess* fits within the genre (or not as the case may be).

Their deliberations will also enable them to make informed contributions to the whole-class discussion about traditional tales which will take place afterwards.

TEXT INTRODUCTION

Teacher:

- Encourages pupils to predict the text type from the front cover. For example:

  Look at the front and back cover, what type of text do you think this is? Do you think the 'Paper Bag Princess' might be different?

  (Refer back to whole-class work on features of Traditional Tales.)

STRATEGY CHECK

- Teacher identifies some of the unusual vocabulary and models how meaning can be inferred from the context.
- Teacher asks pupils to read the story and think about similarities and differences to other traditional tales they know well.

INDEPENDENT READING

- Each child works with their own copy of the text.
- During reading the teacher observes, prompts and praises each child in turn, helping develop pupils' independent reading strategies. The teacher particularly helps pupils to use context clues to infer meaning of words that have been decoded by pupil.

  Can I stop you a moment before moving on to the next page? What do you think the word fiercest means? How do you know? What does it tell you about the dragon?

RETURNING TO THE TEXT/RESPONSE TO THE TEXT

- The teacher works with the group on specific teaching points, starting with the reinforcement of the reading strategy:

  I really liked the way you explained to me how you worked out the meaning of that word. Can you tell the rest of the group how you did it?

  What did you notice about the similarities and differences between other traditional tales you know?

- Teacher tabulates some responses on flipchart (or large piece of paper) under the two headings 'similar' and 'different'.

- Teacher extends understanding and encourages personal response by asking:

  Did you like what the author has done in rewriting the traditional tale like this? Is it successful? Why/Why not?

LINK TO INDEPENDENT WORK/FURTHER READING

- Teacher asks group to continue to brainstorm similarities and differences, either as a whole group or in pairs.

Or

- Asks pupils to write down individually what they thought about the differences they found and whether the author was successful in creating a different type of traditional tale, giving some reasons for their opinion.

GUIDED READING

YEAR 3

HUMOROUS POETRY

WHO'S BEEN SLEEPING IN MY PORRIDGE?
Colin McNaughton

Walker (2000)

ISBN 0744530997

'A book of daft poems and pictures'

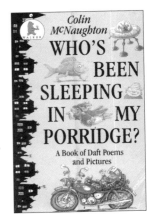

TEACHING OBJECTIVES

- To select, prepare, read aloud and recite by heart poetry that plays with language or entertains.
- To recognise rhyme, alliteration and other patterns of sound that create effects.
- To use awareness of grammar to decipher new or unfamiliar words, e.g. to predict from the text, read on, leave a gap and reread: to use these strategies in conjunction with knowledge of phonemes, word recognition, graphic knowledge and context when reading.

TEXT SELECTION NOTES

Colin McNaughton is one of the best known and most prolific authors of stories and poems for this age group. This anthology of poems and illustrations is typical of his work. Children find much pleasure in the humour of the rhymes and their accompanying pictures. There are many poems in this anthology that could be used as the basis for a guided reading session.

'When I Grow Up' has been chosen because of its strong rhyming patterns, repetition of words and lines and the close relation of pictures and stanzas which underpin the humour.

The repeating pattern of the lines gives strong support for reading cues, particularly grammar, and enables a clear explanation about how each reading 'searchlight' enables us to problem-solve when reading unfamiliar words.

In addition, the structure of the stanzas/rhyming pattern can be easily imitated if pupils are asked to compose their own stanzas for a group poem.

TEXT INTRODUCTION

Teacher:
- Introduces book and author.
- Outlines teaching objectives.
- Asks pupils to turn to the poem 'When I Grow Up' (page 100 of the anthology).
- Tells pupils that they are going to look for the rhyme scheme in each stanza.
- Reads the first two stanzas aloud to pupils and discusses rhyme patterns.

STRATEGY CHECK

Teacher:
- Covers the last word in stanza 3 or 4 with a post-it note.
- Asks pupils to predict what the missing word could be and then uncovers the word and checks.
- Discusses the different reading strategies that they have used.
- Discusses relation of each stanza to its accompanying picture.
- Directs pupils' attention to how the poem should be read aloud by modelling.
- Explains that when pupils have finished reading this poem they can make up another stanza following the same pattern.

INDEPENDENT READING

- Children work with their own copy of the text.
- During reading the teacher observes, prompts and praises. Teacher particularly listens to how children use the rhythm of the stanzas as they read aloud.
- Teacher supports each pupil in turn, picking up problems, helping problem-solve, keeping on task.

RETURNING TO THE TEXT

- Teacher works with the groups on specific teaching points:

  I really liked the way you read the poem. Would you read the last three stanzas to the group? We will listen to how you read clearly, fluently and using the rhythm of the poem.

  In what ways do we read this differently compared to a story?

- One or two pupils share their own, orally composed stanzas.

LINK TO INDEPENDENT ACTIVITY/FURTHER READING

- Pupils individually write their own stanzas following the pattern of 'When I Grow Up'. These can then be compiled in a group poem and read out as a performance to the rest of the class in the plenary.

Or

- Pupils browse through the poems in the book, select a poem, learn it by heart and recite it to an audience.

GUIDED READING

YEAR 3

STORIES BY THE SAME AUTHOR

More challenging

HAVE YOU SEEN WHO'S JUST MOVED IN NEXT DOOR TO US?
Colin McNaughton

Walker Books (1993)

ISBN 0744530431

TEACHING OBJECTIVES

Stories by the same author:
- To compare and contrast works by the same author e.g. different stories, sequels using same characters in new settings.
- To compare forms or types of humour: word play, puns, nonsense verse.

TEXT SELECTION NOTES

Colin McNaughton has been selected because his work is accessible to readers who have not yet acquired full fluency and also because it is sufficiently challenging to engage more able readers through his use of sharp wit and humour. Characteristics of McNaughton's work include:
- meaning carried in the interplay between text and illustration
- comic-strip style stories
- suspense through dramatic irony
- word play
- puns
- speech bubbles and thought balloons
- stories in verse with strong end rhyme.

LINK TO WHOLE-CLASS WORK

- A display of Colin McNaughton's books and related resources is available in the book area.
- The teacher has read *Have You Seen Who's Just Moved in Next Door to Us?* during his regular read-aloud session at the end of the day.
- In a sequence of shared reading lessons Colin McNaughton's *Preston Pig* stories have been read.
- Guided by the teacher the class have brainstormed a list of typical features in Colin McNaughton's work (see above).
- During independent activities the children have searched for supporting information using web sites that the teacher has already located.
- In shared and guided writing they have written to McNaughton's publishers requesting information and publicity material covering the non-fiction objectives for Year 3 Term 3 *Read and write a range of letters*.
- Whole-class sentence work has included conversion of direct speech from speech bubbles into conventional presentation of direct speech using punctuation.
- In shared reading the class have discussed aspects of the books that they have found amusing and have started to classify different types of humour.

GUIDED READING

The focus for the lesson is to guide the group in identifying the different types of humour that Colin McNaughton employs, building on the shared reading lesson.

TEXT INTRODUCTION

- Teacher draws attention to story type and reinforces prediction as a strategy by asking: Can we tell what type of story we are going to read from the front cover? Scary? Sad? Funny? What makes you think that?

  (Although the front cover depicts a collection of monsters and ghosts their expressions and cartoon-style drawing suggest humour rather than horror.)

- Teacher reads first two verses to the group using expression to pick up rhyme and rhythm.

STRATEGY CHECK

Teacher:
- Talks about what is happening on the first page drawing attention to the speech bubbles at the bottom of the page and the 'sold' notice on the house next door.
- Draws out how these cues help support the gleaning of meaning from the text.

INDEPENDENT READING

- Children read pages 2–5. Teacher prompts and praises as appropriate, drawing attention to rhyme and rhythm to aid reading.
- The group discusses points of interest in the pictures.

RETURNING TO THE TEXT

Teacher:
- Asks: What makes the book funny?
- Helps pupils classify types of humour using a prepared grid. Some free columns are left for children to insert their own ideas.

word play	names	characters	nonsense	other

Teacher uses supplementary questions to extend the children's thinking. For example drawing out the following:

Humour in the illustrations: coffin-shaped windows
Word play:
- at the Dumptys': *eggstraordinary*, *eggsactly*, how *eggciting*
- chinese whispers: new neighbours pass it on; nude neighbours pass it on...
- puns: 'I've been framed'

Nonsense words: fwaderbal, fladoop, balloo, yuck
References to known stories and rhymes: Duke of York marching up and down the stairs
Comic characters: Mr Backwards, Hells Angels doing embroidery and housework.

Teacher finishes by asking the question: What have we learnt about the different techniques writers can employ to make their stories funny?

LINK TO INDEPENDENT WORK/ FURTHER READING

In pairs the children continue reading the book aloud to each other. They identify humorous aspects of the story and record on the grid. Teacher returns briefly to this group during the plenary for feedback.

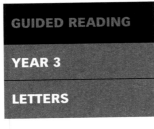

THE JOLLY POCKET POSTMAN
Janet and Allan Ahlberg

Heinemann (1995)

ISBN 0434969427

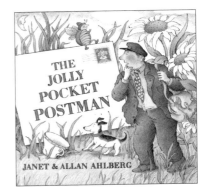

TEACHING OBJECTIVE	Read examples of letters written for a range of purposes.

TEXT SELECTION NOTES

The Ahlbergs' *The Jolly Postman* is a modern classic of children's literature. The rhyming text tells the story of a day in the life of the Jolly Postman and is interspersed with removable copies of letters from his mail bag. *The Jolly **Pocket** Postman* has a similar appeal to the earlier book; the gallery of characters the Postman meets on his delivery round is extended to include those from children's classics such as *Alice in Wonderland* and *The Wizard of Oz*. The selection from the mail bag includes a circular, a spidergram, an airmail letter and a 'get well' message.

CONTEXT FOR GUIDED READING

- A stimulus wall display featuring many different types of letter writing, cards, e-mail and text messages has been set up in the classroom. The pupils have contributed to the display, bringing examples from home. Copies of *The Jolly Postman*, *The Jolly Pocket Postman* and *The Jolly Christmas Postman* are available for the children to read for independent and paired reading.
- For homework the pupils surveyed the range of letters and other mail that their households received in one day. A wall chart was constructed from the information gathered.
- An extension display of books and resources containing the characters (different versions of *Alice in Wonderland* and *The Wizard of Oz*) is set up in the class library.
- The teacher has read *The Jolly Postman* and *The Jolly Pocket Postman* during read-aloud sessions.
- Previous shared, guided and independent reading and writing activities relating to The Jolly Postman have been carried out.
- The class have already written personal letters and are familiar with layout and the conventions for writing the address.

THE GUIDED READING LESSON

In this session the teacher is reinforcing the idea that letters and messages are sent for a range of purposes. Copies of *The Jolly Postman* and *The Jolly Pocket Postman* are available.

TEXT INTRODUCTION

Teacher:
- Gives brief summary of the story.
- Opens the book and reads from 'No fear!' the Postman cries. You scamp…'
- Covers up one word in each rhyming couplet: agree, nose, by, guess.
- Reads 'Then just when the Postman's about to –, He's blown away by sneeze number three'

STRATEGY CHECK

Teacher:
- Points out to pupils that to read the missing words you can use the rhyme to help you. Draws attention to the first example:

  Look at the first one
  'Just when the Postman's about to –
  He's blown away by sneeze number three.'
  Can you find a word that will fit in the gap?
- Asks the group to confirm whether the words chosen make sense and fit with the rhyme pattern.
- Repeats process for one or two other couplets.
  Gives specific instructions:

  Read up to 'For whom it is intended? Guess.' Try to use the reading strategy we have practised.

INDEPENDENT READING

- Pupils read independently.
- Teacher listens to each pupil in turn prompting pupils to use reading strategies when necessary.

RETURNING TO THE TEXT

Teacher:
- Asks the group to list some of the reasons that we might send letters through the post.
- Referring to the suggestions, helps pupils consider whether it is more efficient to send some messages by other means (telephone, e-mail, text messaging).
- Asks children for examples in the Jolly Postmen books.

Suggestions might include some of the following responses:
- People like to receive greetings cards e.g. get well messages that they can display (has anyone in the group ever received an e-card from a friend?).
- We like to send and receive postcards that show where we have been on holiday.
- Official letters might need to be recorded with proof of delivery or receipt e.g. solicitor's letters.
- Advertising – circulars through the letterbox might reach a wider audience than those posted via the internet. Not everyone has access to the internet.
- Sometimes we send small gifts, cheques and postal orders through the post.

Teacher summarises the main advantages of sending letters through the post and the main advantages of sending messages through electronic communication systems.

LINK TO INDEPENDENT WORK/ FURTHER READING

- Choose one of the suggestions listed above (greetings card/postcard/official letter/advertisement).
- Explain the task: to write a letter in this style.
- Briefly direct attention to form of address, style and tone of language, possible content, how the letter can appropriately be closed.

YEAR 3 BOOK LIST	Author/Editor	Publisher/Date	ISBN
FICTION			
3 Billy Goats Gruff	Ted Dewan	Hippo 1995	0590559168
A Bargain for Frances	Russell Hoban	Picture Mammoth 1992	0749712317
Amazing Grace	Mary Hoffman	Frances Lincoln 1993	0711206996
Ambulance	Robina Beddes Willson	Corgi 1999	0552546291
Anancy and Mr. Dry-bone	Fiona French	Francis Lincoln 1998	0711213844
Art You're Magic	Sam McBratney	Walker 1994	0744531039
B J Dog	Stan Cullimore, Wendy Body (ed.)	Longman Book Project (Longman) 1994	0582121183
Baabra Lamb	Geraldine McCaughrean, Wendy Body (ed.)	Longman Book Project (Longman) 1994	0582121663
Beating the Drought	Diana Noonan	Redcliffe Publishing 1999	0478245521
Bertha's Secret Battle	John Coldwell, Doffy Weir (illus.)	Oxford Reading Tree 1998	019918786X
Beware the Killer Coat	Susan Gates	Walker 1995	0744536669
Billy Fishbone	Martin Waddell, Wendy Body (ed.)	Longman Book Project (Longman) 1994	0582121728
Borka	John Burningham	Red Fox 1999	0099400677
Care of Henry	Anne Fine	Walker 1997	0744552583
Cup Final Kid	Martin Waddell	Walker 1997	0744552400
Dave and the Tooth Fairy	Verna Wilkins	Tamarind 1993	1870516133
Dear Greenpeace	Simon Jones	Walker 1991	074451536X
Degas and the Little Dancer	Laurence Anholt	Frances Lincoln 1996	0711210748
Descriptions from Dahl	Wendy Body (ed.)	Longman 2000	0582433088
Dogger	Shirley Hughes	Julia MacRae 1999	1856817644
Dragon Ride	Helen Cresswell	Puffin 1989	0140324801
Dreamboat Zing	Philip Ridley	Puffin 1996	0140372822
Eerie Encounters	Judy Waite	Literacy World /Heinemann 2000	0435118218
Escape!	Pauline Cartwright	Redcliffe Publishing 1999	0478245610
Free the Whales	Jamie Rix	Walker 1997	0744541840
Greedy Cat and the Birthday Cake	Joy Cowley	Redcliffe Publishing 1999	0478245629
Have You Seen Who's Just Moved in Next Door to Us?	Colin McNaughton	Walker 1993	0744530431
Hmm...	Colin McNaughton	Picture Lions 2000	0006646557
Horrible Baby	Jean Ure, Wendy Body (ed.)	Longman Book Project (Longman) 1994	0582121590
Impossible Parents	Brian Patten	Walker 1995	0744536685
Jamaica and Brianna	Janita Havill	Mammoth 1995	0749725044
Jilly's Days	Brian Moses, Wendy Body (ed.)	Longman Book Project (Longman) 1994	0582121531
Jolly Roger	Colin McNaughton	Walker 1988	0744510112
Jug Ears	Jean Ure, Wendy Body (ed.)	Longman Book Project (Longman) 1994	0582121582
Jumble Joan	Rose Impey	Young Lions 1993	0006748511
Katie Morag and the Two Grandmothers	Mairi Hedderwick	Red Fox 1999	0099118718
Katie Morag Delivers the Mail	Mairi Hedderwick	Red Fox 1997	0099220725
Kung Fu Katy and the Horrors	Sally Ann Lever, Wendy Body (ed.)	Longman Book Project (Longman) 1994	0582121493
Little Bear and the Wish Fish	Debi Gliori	Frances Lincoln 1995	0711209421
Little Inchkin	Fiona French	Frances Lincoln 2000	0711216223
Lucy's Picture	Nicola Moon	Orchard 1994	1852136014
Master Money and the Millionaire	Allan Ahlberg	Puffin 1981	0140312463
Miss Brick the Builders' Baby	Allan Ahlberg	Puffin 1981	0140312420
Mole In A Hole	Rita Golden Gelman	Random House 2001	0679890378
Mrs Cockle's Cat	Philippa Pearce	Puffin 1995	0140321187
Mrs Jolly's Joke Shop	Allan Ahlberg	Puffin 1998	0140323473
Never Kiss Frogs	Robert Leeson, David Simonds (illus.)	Puffin 1993	0140347402
Pet Rescue	Judy Waite	Literacy World /Heinemann 2000	0435116584 (Pack of 6)
Phew, Sidney	Rose Impey	Orchard 1994	1852136804
Pirate Plays	Stan Cullimore	Pelican Longman 2000	0582344948
Posh Watson	Gillian Cross	Walker 1996	0744547393
Poupette	Jean Ure, Wendy Body (ed.)	Longman Book Project (Longman) 1994	0582121604
Princess Smartypants	Babette Cole	Puffin 1996	0140555269
Rachel and the Difference Thief	Malorie Blackman, Wendy Body (ed.)	Longman Book Project (Longman) 1994	0582121523

YEAR 3 BOOK LIST	Author/Editor	Publisher/Date	ISBN
Rainbows All Around	Suzanne Hardin	Redcliffe Publishing 1999	0478245661
Rama and the Demon King	Jessica Souhami	Frances Lincoln 1998	0711211582
Rosie's Babies	Martin Waddell	Walker 1990	0744509769
Rumpelstiltskin	retold by Brenda Parkes	Literacy Links – Kingscourt 1990	0732704405
Settings and Cliffhangers	Martin Waddell	Longman 2000	0582344921
Smugglers Mourne	Martin Waddell, Wendy Body (ed.)	Longman Book Project (Longman) 1994	0582121957
Something Special	Nicola Moon	Orchard 1996	1860390862
Stranger Danger	Anne Fine	Puffin 2000	014130913X
Taking the Cat's Way Home	Jan Mark	Walker 1995	0744536677
The Bad Dad List	Anna Kenna	Redcliffe Publishing 1999	0174021976
The Baked Bean Kids	Ann Pilling	Walker 1994	0744531837
The Bears who Stayed Indoors	Susanna Gretz	Black 1999	0713652268
The Day Poppy said 'Yes'	Moira Andrew, Wendy Body (ed.)	Longman Book Project (Longman) 1994	0582121671
The Diary of a Killer Cat	Anne Fine	Penguin 1994	0140369317
The Family Who Won A Million & Other Family Stories	Alison Sage	Red Fox 1997	0099668718
The Finger Eater	Dick King-Smith	Walker 1994	0744530911
The Fisherman and his Wife	retold by Brenda Parkes	Literacy Links – Kingscourt	0790106508 (pack of 6)
The Frog Prince Continued	John Scieszka, Steve Johnson (illus.)	Puffin 1992	014054285X
The Ghost Teacher	Tony Bradman	Corgi Pups 1996	0552529761
The Golden Goose	Jacob and Wilhelm Grimm	North South Books 1999	0735811989
The Hairy Canaries and Other Nonsense	Martin Waddell, Wendy Body (ed.)	Longman Book Project (Longman) 1994	0582122252
The Haunting of Pip Parker	Anne Fine	Walker 1994	0744530938
The Jolly Pocket Postman	Janet and Allan Ahlberg	Heinemann 1995	0434969427
The Leopard's Drum	Jessica Souhami	Frances Lincoln 2000	071121641X
The Magic Boathouse	Sam Llewellyn	Walker 1995	0744536863
The Magic Finger	Roald Dahl	Puffin (new edn) 2001	0141311290
The Pain and the Great One	Judy Blume	Pan Books 1998	0330296310
The Paper Bag Princess	Robert Munsch	Little Hippo 1999	0590711261
The Queen's Knickers	Nicholas Allan	Red Fox 1993	0091764688
The Robodog	Frank Rodgers	Puffin 2001	0141310308
The Shopping Basket	John Burningham	Red Fox 1992	0099899302
The Snow Maze	Jan Mark	Walker 1994	074453092X
The Sock Gobbler and other stories	Barbara Berge et al.	Redcliffe Publishing 1999	0478245696
The Three Little Wolves and the Big Bad Pig	Eugene Triviazas and Helen Oxenbury	Mammoth 1994	0749725052
Webster and the Treacle Toffee	Sheila Lavelle, Wendy Body (ed.)	Longman Book Project (Longman) 1994	0582121485
Willy the Wizard	Anthony Browne	Red Fox 1996	0099537613
Wish You Were Here	Martina Selway	Red Fox 1996	0099383713
NON-FICTION			
All About Touch	Irene Yates	Belitha Press 1998	1855617765
Bridging the Gap	Steve Miller	Redcliffe Publishing 2000	0478245556
Canoe Diary	Nic Bishop	Redcliffe Publishing 1999	0478245564
Cat Talk	Don Long	Redcliffe Publishing 1999	0478245752
How a Big Book is Made	Emma Lynch	Literacy World /Heinemann 1998	0435096532
Incredible Insects	Claire Llewellyn	Literacy World /Heinemann 1998	0435096516
Letters to Edward	Wendy Body	Longman 2000	0582346886
Make it with Paper	Moira Andrew	Longman 2000	0582346053
Making the Past into Presents	Jo Brooker	Literacy World /Heinemann 1998	0435096494
Measuring the Weather	Bill Gaynor	Redcliffe Publishing 2000	047812463
Pizza	Brian Moses	Wayland 1992	0750205180
Seal	Meredith Hooper	Cambridge University Press 1996	0521477891
Teacher	Margaret Hudson	Heinemann 1996	0431063354
The Life of a Duck	Josephine Croser	Magic Bean – Era Publications 1989	0947212310
The Search for the Tutankhamen	Jane Shuter	Literacy World /Heinemann 1998	0435118919
The Shapes of Water	Gillian Shannon and Clare Bowes	Redcliffe Publishing 1999	0478245688
There's No Place Like Home	David Hill	Redcliffe Publishing 2000	0478245718

YEAR 3 BOOK LIST	Author/Editor	Publisher/Date	ISBN
What's Cooking?	Pauline Cartwright	Redcliffe Publishing 2000	0478245726
What's Living at Your Place?	Bruce Chapman	Redcliffe Publishing 2000	0478245734
POETRY			
A Door to Secrets	Tony Mitton	Cambridge Reading Scheme 1998	0521498414
A First Poetry Book	John L. Foster *et al*. (ed.)	Oxford 1979	0199181128
Cats Sleep Anywhere	Eleanor Farjeon, Anne Mortimer (illus.)	Frances Lincoln 1998	0711212864
Dog Days: Rhymes Around the Year	Jack Prelutsky	Bantam Books 2001	0440417538
Down By The River	Grace Hallworth	Mammoth 1997	0749730250
Give Yourself a Hug	Grace Nichols	Puffin 1996	0140372180
Going Barefoot	Judith Thisman	*A First Book of Poetry* – Oxford 1979	0199181128
Lunch Boxes Don't Fly	Michael Rosen, Korky Paul (illus.)	Puffin 1999	0141300205
My Dad, your Dad	Kit Wright	*The Kingfisher Book of Comic Verse* – Kingfisher 1991	0862727855
On The Ning Nang Nong	Spike Milligan	*Noisy Poems*, collected by Jill Bennett – Oxford 1993	0192760637
Pigs Aplenty, Pigs Galore	David McPhail	Picture Puffin 1997	0140553134
Please Mrs Butler	Allan Ahlberg	Puffin 1984	0140314946
Poems for 9 year olds and under	Kit Wright	Penguin 1999	0140314903
Silly Poems	John Foster	Hippo Books 1998	0590192515
The Broken Toys	James Kirkup	*A First Book of Poetry* – Oxford 1979	0199181128
The Circle of Days	Reeve Lindbergh, Cathie Falstead (illus.)	Walker 2000	0744572843
The Marrog	R. C. Scriven	*A First Book of Poetry* – Oxford 1979	0199181128
The Sounds In The Evening	Eleanor Farjeon	*The Puffin Book of 20th Century Children's Verse* – Puffin 1991	0140322361
There Was An Old Man	James Kirkup	*A First Book of Poetry* – Oxford 1979	0199181128
Uncle Billy Being Silly	Michael Rosen, Korky Paul (illus.)	Puffin 2001	0141300213
When Dad Felt Bad	Charles Causley	*A First Book of Poetry* – Oxford 1979	0199181128
Who's Been Sleeping in my Porridge?	Colin McNaughton	Walker 2000	0744530997
MORE CHALLENGING LITERARY TEXTS FOR YEAR 3 PUPILS			
Alone in the Grange	Gregory Harrison	*A First Book of Poetry* – Oxford 1979	0199181128
Grandpa Chatterji	Jamila Gavin	Mammoth 1994	0749717165
The True Story of the 3 Little Pigs	Jon Scieszka	Puffin 1991	0140540563
The Upside Down Mice & Other Animal Stories	Jane Merer (ed.)	Collins 1996	0006751148
The Worst Witch	Jill Murphy	Puffin 1974	0140311084

YEAR 4 EXEMPLAR GUIDED READING SESSIONS

GUIDED READING

YEAR 4

PERSUASIVE TEXTS

ADVERTS FROM *THE DANDY*

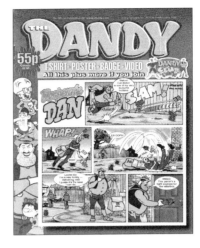

TEACHING OBJECTIVE

- To evaluate advertisements for their impact, appeal and honesty, focusing in particular on how information about the product is presented: exaggerated claims, tactics for grabbing attention, linguistic devices, e.g. puns, jingles, alliteration, invented words.

TEXT SELECTION NOTES

Children's comics and magazines are a rich source of persuasive texts (i.e. explicit advertising). One copy of *The Beano* or *The Dandy* will provide a group of six pupils with at least one full advertisement each.

Each one has a limited amount of text so can be read quickly, but the pupils can consider all of them if the comic has been dismembered.

Although the following exemplar guided reading session has been written with two specific advertisements as its textual focus, it provides a structure whereby any advertisement from children's comics and magazines can be approached.

TEXT INTRODUCTION

- Both advertisements are given to pupils.
- Children are encouraged to identify the text type and introduce the texts to themselves.
- Teacher explains that they will read both advertisements and then discuss some of the following:

    What is the purpose of the advertisements? What are they trying to persuade you to do?

    Who are they trying to persuade? Parents? Children? Boys? Girls?

    How do they grab your attention and make you want to read on?

INDEPENDENT READING

- Each child works with his/her own copies of the texts.
- During reading teacher observes, prompts and praises, particularly focusing on the pre-set questions.

    What form does the strip cheese advert take? (i.e. comic strip). Does it make you want to read it? What kind of jokes does it contain? (i.e. puns, etc.) Does it make you want to buy some? Why/why not?

RETURNING TO THE TEXT/RESPONSE TO THE TEXT

- Teacher asks the questions posed in the introduction, particularly selecting responses which illustrate the tactics for grabbing attention – large print, colourful letters, emphasis on what you get for very little money (the Dandy Club) as well as the different forms of the two advertisements.

LINK TO FOLLOW-UP INDEPENDENT WORK/ FURTHER READING

- Pupils closely read each text.
- Pupils list or highlight the reasons given for the purchasing of each product on offer:
    why you should eat strip cheese
    why you should join the Dandy Club.
- They decide which is the most persuasive and give two reasons to justify their answer.

Or

- Pupils identify all the puns in the strip cheese advertisement and list them. Make up two or three more which could have been included in this advertisement (e.g. This is our 'cue to leave'. What's that ping pong I smell?)

COME AND JOIN US IN

THE DANDY CLUB

© D. C. THOMSON & CO., LTD., 2000

HERE'S WHAT YOU GET IF YOU JOIN THE DANDY CLUB

YOUR OWN PERSONAL MEMBERSHIP CARD AND CERTIFICATE.

AN EXCLUSIVE T-SHIRT — ONLY AVAILABLE BY JOINING THE CLUB. YOU CAN'T BUY THIS T-SHIRT DESIGN IN THE SHOPS!

A GREAT CLUB POSTER FEATURING YOUR DANDY FAVOURITES.

A VIDEO FEATURING 10 (YES, TEN) OF BANANAMAN'S CRAZY CARTOON ADVENTURES.

A SPECIAL CLUB BADGE

A STINGER CHEW BAR FROM *Swizzels Matlow*

2 YEARS MEMBERSHIP! FOR JUST £12

CONTENTS OF THE PACK WOULD BE WORTH AT LEAST £25 IF BOUGHT IN THE SHOPS.

All of this great Club gear will be sent in a handy bag — it's ideal for holding your swimming stuff or sports gear.
AND THERE'S STILL MORE!
You'll receive Dandy Club newsletters filled with fun stories and gags and EXCLUSIVE OFFERS for DANDY CLUB MEMBERS ONLY. And on your birthday, you'll be sent a special birthday card from the Club.

STINGER
TEMPTINGLY TROPICAL

I'M AN OFFICIAL MEMBER OF DANDY CLUB

THIS BODY BELONGS TO A DANDY

ADULT CLUB PACK AVAILABLE AT £13 (U.K.) AND £15 FOR ALL OVERSEAS REQUESTS (INC EIRE.)

● Please note: The contents of the Welcome pack may change from time to time.
● Please allow up to 28 days for delivery.
● Membership of **The Dandy Club** lasts for 2 years.
● Members will each receive newsletters and 2 birthday cards during their membership.
● To join The Dandy Club, simply complete the coupon — remembering you MUST get your parent or guardian to sign it — and send it to:-
THE DANDY CLUB P.O. BOX 6757 DUNDEE DD1 9UE

The Dandy Club Membership Request

PLEASE PRINT CLEARLY IN INK

First Name ....

Surname ....

Address ....

....

....

....

Postcode ....

Phone No ....

Date of Birth ...../...../.....
Day Month Year

☐ Boy ☐ Girl

T-shirt size

Junior — To fit height

a) ☐ small 122-128cm
b) ☐ medium 134-140cm
c) ☐ large 146-152cm

Adult — chest size

d) ☐ medium 100 cm
e) ☐ large 110 cm
f) ☐ extra large 120 cm

Remittance (Sterling only. Do not send cash). £12 ☐ £13 ☐ £15 ☐ (All overseas)
Cheques and Postal Orders made payable to D.C. Thomson & Co., Ltd.
I wish to pay by Visa/Mastercard/Switch; please charge to my account.
My card number is

☐☐☐☐ ☐☐☐☐ ☐☐☐☐ ☐☐☐☐ ☐☐☐☐

Valid from ☐ / ☐ Expiry date ☐ / ☐ SWITCH Card Issue No. if applicable ☐☐

Card-holder's signature ....

Parent/Guardian's Signature (If under 15) ....
Tick box if you do not wish to receive special offers or promotional material from selected companies ☐
DDY1

THE OWL TREE
SESSION 2

TEACHING OBJECTIVES

- To identify the main characteristics of the key characters, drawing on the text to justify views, and using information to predict actions.
- To reinforce contextual strategy for problem-solving the meaning of specific, unknown vocabulary from text.
- To practise silent reading.

TEXT INTRODUCTION

Teacher:
- Outlines learning objectives.
- Checks all children have read to the end of chapter 3.
- Asks pupils to identify main characters and then to give their impressions of them.
- Tells pupils to use their notes of words/phrases describing the characters as evidence for their opinions.
- Prompts pupils to use other sources of evidence (i.e. speech and actions) for their views of the main characters: You think Joe is a 'wimp'; what does he do or say that makes you think that?

STRATEGY CHECK

Teacher:
- Reminds pupils about problem-solving strategies for unusual words.
- Sets pupils off reading with explicit instructions:
- Read chapter 4.
  - Add more evidence to your lists of character detail.
  - What does the word *scornful* mean on p. 36?

INDEPENDENT READING

- During reading teacher intervenes with individuals, offering explicit support for decoding and problem-solving strategies, and continues to ask inferential questions about pupils' view of the characters.

RETURNING TO THE TEXT

Teacher:
- Discusses any general issues about self-correction/problem-solving strategies.
- Asks pupils if they have found more evidence from the text to support/undermine their earlier stated views of the character. Have their views changed or not?
- Discusses meaning of *scornful*.
- Reinforces again contextual cues as problem-solving strategy if needed.

FOLLOW-UP INDEPENDENT TASK/ FURTHER READING

Teacher:
- Gives specific tasks to be completed before next week's guided reading session:

Please read to the end of chapter 6.
Choose one of the main characters (now including Mr Rock) and predict what they will do in the last part of the book. You should be prepared to justify your predictions by referring to what you already know about those characters. Make notes in your reading notebooks. Your notes will be used in the next session.

THE OWL TREE
SESSION 3

TEACHING OBJECTIVES

- To identify the main characteristics of the key characters, drawing on the text to justify views, and using information to predict actions.
- To reinforce contextual strategy for problem-solving the meaning of specific, unknown vocabulary from text.
- To practise silent reading.

INTRODUCTION (INCLUDING RESPONDING TO THE TEXT)

Teacher:
- Outlines learning objectives.
- Checks all pupils have read to the end of chapter 6.
- Takes each of the main characters in turn and asks a child to predict briefly what that character will do in the final section of the book.
- Prompts pupils to draw on their notes/evidence to justify their predictions: Do you think Granny Diamond will be able to save the owl tree? What makes you think she will stand up to Mr Rock?
- Reminds pupils that they will be talking about the meaning of some specific vocabulary as they read independently.
- Sets children off reading with explicit instructions:

  Read chapter 7.
  As you read, are the predictions you made the correct ones? What confirms your predictions and what is different?

INDEPENDENT READING AND STRATEGY CHECK

Teacher:
- Listens to each child read a short extract as others read silently.
- Checks occasionally that pupils can use contextual cues for unravelling the meaning of specific vocabulary.

RETURNING TO THE TEXT

Teacher:
- Gives feedback on pupils' progress in using contextual cues over the three sessions. Asks them what they think they have learnt.
- Discusses whether predictions about characters have been borne out as they read. Discusses any discrepancies.
- Summarises what pupils have learnt, referring to learning objectives for the three-week sequence of guided reading.

FOLLOW-UP INDEPENDENT WORK/ FURTHER READING

Teacher:
- Gives specific tasks to be completed before next week's guided reading session:

  Read to the end of the book.
  Consider: Why did Mr Rock change his mind?

- Asks pupils to write down two reasons in their reading notebooks.

GUIDED READING

YEAR 4

NON-FICTION HISTORY TEXT

This could be chosen from a selection available to the class, for example:

How We Used to Live: Victorians early and late
David Evans
A & C Black (1990)
ISBN 0713633107

Family Life in Victorian Britain
Richard Wood
Wayland (1994)
ISBN 0750223049

Victorians
Clare Chandler
Wayland (1994)
ISBN 0750212675

A Family in the Thirties
Sue Crawford
Wayland (1988)
ISBN 1852106042

Fifty Years Ago: At home
Karen Bryant-Mole
Wayland (1998)
ISBN 0705223936

Fifty Years Ago: In the high street
Karen Bryant-Mole
Wayland (1999)
ISBN 0750225793

Any history texts which are appropriate to Key Stage 2 and which are in current use on a history topic will be suitable.

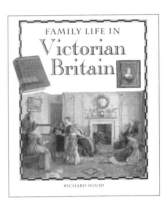

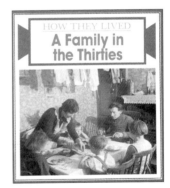

TEACHING OBJECTIVES

Because the particular focus will need to be adapted to the features of the history texts available, these are presented as options.

- To examine the features of non-fiction texts, including the use of illustrations and text, as well as headings, contents page, glossary, index, etc.
- To examine how text is organised in non-narrative accounts.
- To explore the author's position.
- To develop critical responses to non-fiction texts.

CONTEXT FOR GUIDED READING SESSION

It is preferable for each child to see the same double-page spread, but if this is not possible each one should have a non-fiction book relevant to their current work in history.

NOTE

This guided reading exemplar contains options, each one of which could form the basis of a single guided reading session. We are not suggesting that all the following could possibly be covered in one session.

TEXT INTRODUCTION

Teacher:
- Asks pupils to quickly brainstorm the typical features of non-fiction texts: contents pages, glossary, index, headings, and then check whether their texts have these features.
- Discusses the purpose of these books (to convey information).
- Helps pupils to consider whether the information is just in the words, or whether the illustrations also convey information.

For example:

> We're going to see how these books tell us about the Victorians (or the Tudors, or …) and try to learn more about what makes an effective, interesting book. As you read it, think about what grabs your attention on each page.

INDEPENDENT READING

Each child reads two double-page spreads – these books usually have one or two double-page spreads with similar formats for each chapter. When each child has read enough to get a feel for a chapter or section, the teacher moves on to the selected focus.

During reading the teacher observes, prompts and praises. Intervention as children read may focus on the meaning of technical vocabulary or be related to the selected focus.

OPTION 1: FOCUS ON THE ILLUSTRATIONS

RETURNING TO THE TEXT

Possible questions asked by the teacher might include:

- Just look at the pictures. What do you learn from the pictures in your book? Are the pictures photographs, drawings, paintings, or what? How are they different from illustrations in fiction books? How much of the page has illustrations? What's the proportion of illustration to text (words)? Half and half? One third?
- Do the illustrations have captions? Are these necessary? What kinds of information do they convey – purely factual information about the source of the illustration, or a comment or opinion from the author?

Then teacher:

- Encourages pupils to discuss the importance of illustrations for conveying information which is not included in the text. Most books include contemporary photographs, drawings or paintings; some have contemporary cartoons.
- Directs pupils to look at the use of colour and shape of illustrations. For example, some of these books compare current and historical scenes by using colour photographs for current life and black and white for the past.

LINK TO INDEPENDENT WORK/ FURTHER READING

Pupils compose alternative captions for the illustrations/photos/diagrams, which they feel more accurately represent the focus of the information they contain.

OPTION 2: FOCUS ON THE ORGANISATION OF MATERIAL IN THE BOOK

RETURNING TO THE TEXT

Teacher asks:
- Look at the contents page. Is there any reason why the sections are in this order? Just look at any two sections – do they follow on? Is there a story to be followed?
- Is there a main character? Whose lives are being described? Does this make it like a story? Describe two ways it is/isn't.
- Is each double-page spread the same, if so identify the common features. (Heading, subheadings, illustration, text, etc.) Why is this?

LINK TO INDEPENDENT WORK/ FURTHER READING

- Pupils survey two or three other books in their current history topic and look for common features of text structure and page layout.

OPTION 3: USING STRUCTURAL FEATURES TO FIND INFORMATION

RETURNING TO THE TEXT

Teacher:
- Supports pupils as they brainstorm briefly the kinds of questions one might want to find out about in the books. For example: What sports were popular in Victorian times?
- Asks pupils to decide how the structural features of the text will help to locate this information.
- Demonstrates using contents, index, page headings and numbers.
- Explores with pupils whether chapter headings and indexes are well organised, informative and comprehensive. Can the answer be found in illustrations rather than in text? Does the index help when the information is contained in the illustrations?

LINK TO INDEPENDENT WORK/ FURTHER READING

Teacher either:
- Asks pupils in pairs to locate information to answer questions pre-set by the teacher.

Or
- Asks pupils to write three relevant questions for other pupils to use to locate information.

Then briefly draws group together during independent time to discuss how easy this was, whether some books were better than others, and why this might be.

MORE CHALLENGING

OPTION 4: FOCUS ON THE AUTHOR'S POSITION

RETURNING TO THE TEXT

The teacher prompts pupils to consider how the position/views of the author may affect how the text is written/constructed:

- Who wrote this text? Does the book have any information about the author?
- Is he/she qualified/experienced in this subject? How can we find out?
- Does the author have a bias in the way the pages were written, e.g. were poor people/children left out? Are they anywhere else in the book?
- Can we tell anything about the author's stance from the way incidents are described or the captions written for illustration?
- What questions would you like to ask the author of this book?
- Why would you ask him/her that?

LINK TO INDEPENDENT WORK/ FURTHER READING

After brainstorming a few criteria for detecting the author's position through the above discussion, pupils read through the text and decide whether there is any clear position or bias. This can be reported on briefly during the plenary.

OPTION 5: FOCUS ON PARAGRAPH STRUCTURE

RETURNING TO THE TEXT

Teacher:

- Asks pupils to look carefully at any page and examine how the text is broken up.
- Draws pupils' attention to the paragraphs.
- Reads the first sentence in the paragraph. Points out that the structure of paragraphs usually follows a simple pattern. The first sentence (or 'lead' sentence) tells the reader what the paragraph is about and the rest of the paragraph is further detail and/or supporting evidence.
- Asks pupils to reread the pages and quickly identify whether the paragraphs follow this structure. If not there may be 'key words' in the first sentence which identify the focus for the paragraph.
- Prompts discussion as to whether all the paragraphs on the double-page spread are related to each other and how the page heading or chapter title give an overall indication of the content of all the paragraphs.

FOLLOW UP INDEPENDENT WORK/ FURTHER READING

- Teacher asks pupils to construct flow chart summaries for the paragraphs (using lead sentence, but in shortened form) and the relation to page heading, e.g.

```
┌─────────────────┐
│  Page heading   │
└─────────────────┘
         │
         ▼
┌─────────────────┐
│  Paragraph 1    │
└─────────────────┘
         │
         ▼
┌─────────────────┐
│  Paragraph 2    │
└─────────────────┘
         │
         ▼
┌─────────────────┐
│  Paragraph 3    │
└─────────────────┘
```

GUIDED READING	**THE HAGSTONE** David Oakden
YEAR 4	Anglia Young Books (2001)
HISTORICAL STORIES	ISBN 1871173612

THE DAUGHTER
Jacqueline Wilson
In *Centuries of Stories*
Edited by Wendy
Cooling

HarperCollins (1999)

ISBN 006754155

Working with historical fiction texts over two sessions

TEACHING OBJECTIVES

Historical stories and short novels:
- To investigate how historical settings are built up from small details; references to time and place
- To identify the conflict/problem which develops from the historical context.

TEXT SELECTION NOTES

When choosing historical fiction to read with Year 4 children we need to consider whether the point of view is one to which the children will be able to relate. Often a historical novel will be written consciously in a style that gives an impression of being written a long time ago; for some developing readers this may be too challenging. The two stories selected for these guided reading sessions have clear narration and subject content to which children in Year 4 can relate. The point of view is accessible, focusing on the impact of the period on individual children. *The Hagstone* is one in a series of stories expressly written to support the history curriculum and has an overtly didactic intention, while the language and content of Jacqueline Wilson's story, 'The Daughter', is more sophisticated. The vocabulary, sentence structure and content are sufficiently challenging to extend the most able readers in this Year 4 class. The two texts may be used simultaneously with two groups at different achievement levels, using 'The Daughter' with a more advanced group of readers.

The class are studying the Tudors in history and this is the historical context for both stories.

Features of *The Hagstone*

Notes: these contextualise the story (suggesting the book is intended to support the history curriculum)
Time: set in Tudor England during the reign of Queen Elizabeth (1575)
Characters: include rich and poor to give an insight into the different lives
Problem: Tom, a wealthy merchant's son, persuades his mother to let him visit the town fair. He is abducted by a band of rogues and beggars.

LINKS TO WHOLE-CLASS WORK

The class have gathered information from books and other sources and have visited a Tudor house.

TEXT 1: THE HAGSTONE
SESSION 1

TEXT INTRODUCTION

Teacher:
- Briefly explains that the group are going to be reading a story set in Tudor times during guided reading.
- Asks them to consider the title. What do the children think a 'hagstone' is? (Read on to find out!)

STRATEGY CHECK

Teacher:
- Draws from pupils strategies for predicting the meaning of unfamiliar words (e.g. using context, reading on, using linked illustration).
- Prompts pupils to check how they might use these strategies on any unknown words in this text.

INDEPENDENT READING

- Pupils read independently up to: 'Magic tricks made money for the trickster but never for the poor fairgoer'.
- Teacher directs children to think about what facts they can find out about life in Tudor England as they read the text.
- During reading the teacher observes, prompts and praises, in particular checking pupils' understanding of any unusual vocabulary such as *tumblers*. Use context and check in dictionary if necessary.

RETURNING TO THE TEXT

Teacher asks:
- Where does this story take place?
- Is there anything about the setting that is familiar/unfamiliar?

Pupils are asked to say what facts they found out about life in Tudor England. Demonstrate writing facts as bullet points, e.g.

Facts about Tudor England
- travel was difficult
- servants didn't get many holidays
- travelling fairs visited towns

LINK TO INDEPENDENT WORK/ FURTHER READING

Teacher asks pupils to:
- Read up to 'Food had to be brought instead of grown. Things were very different'.
- In the text find four facts about children from rich families and four facts about children from poor families.
- Read the rest of the introduction and chapter 1 in preparation for second session.

TEXT 1: THE HAGSTONE
SESSION 2

INTRODUCTION (INCLUDING RESPONDING TO THE TEXT)

Teacher:
- Reviews previous lesson.
- Asks for initial responses to the first chapter.
- Supports and directs discussion of evidence of the historical setting:
  How can we tell the story is set in the past?

INDEPENDENT READING

Pupils in pairs note down evidence from text that the story is set in the past.

RETURNING TO THE TEXT

Teacher prompts discussion about evidence found. One member of the group collates information on the flipchart.

Evidence in the text is as follows:

Time: explicitly stated 1575
Characters:
> names: Mistress Kett, Master Tom
> occupations: wool merchant, apprentice
> clothes: velvet doublet

Activities:
> hawk for hunting
> town fair
> school subjects.

- Teacher finishes by asking,
  What have you learnt about the Tudors from reading this book so far?
  Do you think it is a good story? What makes you think that?

Pupils are encouraged to justify their opinions.

Teachers' note

The rhyme 'Hark! Hark! the dogs do bark/The Beggars are coming to town' was popular in Elizabethan England and may have referred to the proliferation of beggars. The Opies note that beggars may have been an epithet for the Dutch. See Iona and Peter Opie, *The Oxford English Dictionary of Nursery Rhymes* (London: Oxford University Press, 1951, pp. 152–3) for full notes.

LINK TO INDEPENDENT WORK

- Pupils read to the end of the story independently.
- Pupils note down any further facts about Tudor life, which they discover, in their reading notebooks.

TEXT 2: THE DAUGHTER
SESSION 1

TEXT INTRODUCTION

Teacher:
- Asks one pupil to introduce the text.
- Asks another pupil to summarise the plot.

INDEPENDENT READING

Teacher asks pupils in pairs to make notes recording evidence that the story is set in the past.

RETURNING TO THE TEXT

Teacher leads group discussion drawing out examples of the following:
- time
- place
- character
- central problem (universal or historical?)
- language
- activities engaged in by characters.

Teacher asks:

> Is the problem in this story related to the historical context? Can you think of an example of this problem occurring in a similar situation today?

RESPONDING TO THE TEXT

- Discussion: Should an author be factually accurate when writing an historical story?
- List points for and against.

SESSION 2

INTRODUCTION

Teacher:
- Introduces and sets up a small-group discussion using a statement game to encourage the pupils to think about the relationship between the factual and fictional content of historical fiction.
- Prompts group, in order to foreground their knowledge and experience, to talk briefly about any other historical stories they have read.

INDEPENDENT DISCUSSION

Pupils discuss the statement cards that the teacher has prepared. Possible statements include:
- The facts used in historical fiction have to be accurate.
- We can learn a lot about the past from reading historical stories.
- We learn more about modern ideas than the past when we read historical stories.
- A good imagination is what makes a good historical story.
- Historical stories do not have to be about real events.

RESPONDING TO THE TEXT

Teacher:
- Asks individual pupils to give an opinion about individual statements.
- Encourages other pupils to respond.
- Scribes the group's conclusions.

GUIDED READING

YEAR 4

CLASSIC POETRY

More challenging

NIGHT AND DAY
Robert Louis Stevenson
In A *Child's Garden of Verses*
Illustrated by Brian Wildsmith

Oxford (1966)

ISBN 0192760653

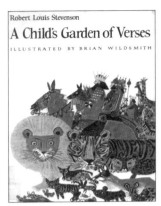

Working with a poem over two sessions

TEACHING OBJECTIVES

- To identify clues which suggest that poems are older, e.g. context, phrases, vocabulary use including archaic words.
- Contextualising a poem in order to enhance the reader's understanding and appreciation.

TEXT SELECTION NOTES

Robert Louis Stevenson told his old nurse 'Cummy', to whom he was devoted, that the poems in the collection were about his childhood. He dedicated it to her as the person who had made his childhood happy. In fact Stevenson had a childhood that was troubled by illness and he described it as being 'In reality a very mixed experience, full of fever, nightmare, insomnia, painful days and interminable nights; and I can speak with less authority of gardens than of that of the land of counterpane.' In these difficult days it was Cummy who took care of him, reciting the psalms and hymns to entertain him. It is likely that through this experience the young Stevenson would have become accustomed to the lilting metrical patterns that are evident in his own poetry.

Stevenson died in 1884; his poems were published in 1885 without pictures. This delightful volume has never been out of print since and has been illustrated by many great illustrators including Henriette Willebeek le Mair (1926), Eve Garnett (1948), Brian Wildsmith (1966) and Michael Foreman (1985).

The teacher has selected this text to introduce the children to 'older' writing as the experiences and emotions of childhood are widely recognisable, the language is straightforward and in spite of the presence of vocabulary that is not in current usage, meanings are relatively easily conveyed.

LINKS TO WHOLE-CLASS WORK

Outside the literacy lesson, the teacher has been reading poems from the collection so the children are already familiar with 'Windy Nights', 'The Land of Counterpane' and 'From A Railway Carriage'.

The children have been stimulated by the poetry to talk about their own childhood experiences. How do they pass the time when they are ill? How do windy days make them feel? They have considered similarities and differences between their own and the poet's experiences.

BEFORE THE SESSIONS

Teacher collects:
- A copy of the poem, 'Night and Day', for each pupil.
- A range of dictionaries (which include the older words in the poem such as 'portal' and 'mortal').

NIGHT AND DAY

When the golden day is done,
    Through the closing portal,
Child and garden, flower and sun,
    Vanish all things mortal.

As the blinding shadows fall,
    As the rays diminish,
Under evening's cloak, they all
    Roll away and vanish.

Garden darkened, daisy shut,
    Child in bed, they slumber –
Glow-worm in the highway rut,
    Mice among the lumber.

In the darkness houses shine,
    Parents move with candles;
Till, on all, the night divine
    Turns the bedroom handles.

Till at last the day begins
    In the east a-breaking,
In the hedges and the whins
    Sleeping birds a-waking.

In the darkness shapes of things,
    Houses, trees, and hedges,
Clearer grow: and sparrow's wings
    Beat on window ledges.

These shall wake the yawning maid;
    She the door shall open –
Finding dew on garden glade
    And the morning broken.

There my garden grows again
    Green and rosy painted,
As at eve behind the pane
    From my eyes it fainted.

Just as it was shut away,
    Toy-like, in the even,
Here I see it glow with day
    Under glowing heaven.

Every path and every plot,
    Every bush of roses,
Every blue forget-me-not
    Where the dew reposes,

'Up!' they cry, 'the day is come
    On the smiling valleys;
We have beat the morning drum;
    Playmate, join your allies!'

Robert Louis Stevenson

NIGHT AND DAY
SESSION 1

TEXT INTRODUCTION (INCLUDING INDEPENDENT READING)

- Pupils read 'Night and Day' through independently without interruption.
- Teacher encourages initial free responses: each child offers their first thought which is not commented on at this stage. This response will probably include children talking about the type of text and some of its features as well as about the meanings they make.

RESPONDING TO THE TEXT

Teacher focuses the discussion on the language of the poem developing ideas suggested in the initial responses:

Focus on language

- While reading the poem, were there any words or phrases that you particularly liked or did not like?
- Can you identify something that happens in the poem that provide clues that it was written a long time ago:
  In the darkness houses shine,
  Parents move with candles
- In the first verse are there any words or phrases that sound rather 'old-fashioned'? e.g. *portal*, *mortal*.
- Do they give the poem a particular feel?

STRATEGY CHECK

Teacher:
- Asks What do you think these words mean?
- Guides the pupils to use context and then the dictionaries to check meanings, reminding them to use first and second letters as appropriate.

Word/Phrase	I think it means	Dictionary definition

Teacher supports pupils' problem-solving strategies by asking:

Reread the first verse to see how these meanings fit.
Has this made the first verse easier to understand?
What is described in the first verse? What makes you say that?

Finishes the session by explaining independent work and discussing how in the follow-up session they will be rereading the poem and assessing how their understanding of it has changed.

FOLLOW-UP INDEPENDENT WORK/ FURTHER READING

- In pairs pupils continue to identify 'old-fashioned' words in the poem. They write down what they think these words mean and then use a dictionary to check the meaning.
- Finally with a partner they reread the poem.

NIGHT AND DAY
SESSION 2

INTRODUCTION (INCLUDING RETURNING/ RESPONDING TO THE TEXT)

Teacher:
- Checks all pupils have completed independent task.
- Gets the pupils to reread the poem aloud. This could be done by asking two or three pupils to reread the poem aloud to the group. Listening to different voices can help develop an appreciation for nuances in interpretation.
- Asks the pupils if their response to the poem is different now that they have worked on the meaning of the 'old-fashioned' words.

   Have you changed your minds about the meaning of the poem? How? Why?
   Did you read the poem differently to the first time? Again, how and why?

- Explains that working on the poem in this way helps clarify what we think the poem means and affects the way we read it.

FOLLOW-UP INDEPENDENT TASK

Teacher:
- Asks pupils in fours (or pairs, depending on the size of the group) to prepare a reading of the poem for presenting to the class.
- Explains that they will have to consider the following when preparing their reading:
   How will the lines be spoken to create the right mood of nightfall and then night turning into day?
   Will voices be soft or loud? Fast or slow?
   How will they bring out the rhythm of the poem?
   Who will speak which lines?

IN THE PLENARY OF THE LITERACY HOUR

The group performs the prepared readings.

Teacher:
- Asks group to talk about decisions they made about how to read the poem (or a particular line of the poem).
- Encourages the class to evaluate the work. What sounded good? What might be improved and how?

LINK TO WHOLE-CLASS WORK

- More complex examples of classic poetry such as:
   Walter de la Mare, 'Tartary'
   Robert Burns, 'My Heart's in the Highlands'
   William Blake, 'The Tiger'
   Rudyard Kipling, 'A Smuggler's Song'.
- Comparison of child's eye view of the world in Robert Louis Stevenson with a contemporary poet, Michael Rosen for example.
- In shared writing write poems based on the experiences that have been discussed and compare language the children use with Stevenson's language.

THE MALFEASANCE
Alan Bold

In *The Oxford Book of Story Poems*

Oxford (1999)

0192762125

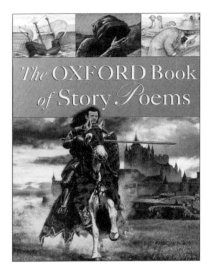

TEACHING OBJECTIVES

- To discuss aspects of poetic form, to identify patterns of rhyme and verse, and to read poetry aloud effectively.
- To distinguish between rhyming and non-rhyming poetry and comment on the impact and layout.

TEXT SELECTION NOTES

'The Malfeasance' is a powerful and humorous modern poem with a serious theme that becomes apparent as we read it through. The theme can be summarised by the aphorism 'we have nothing to fear but fear itself'.

The language used to describe the Malfeasance quickly builds a detailed picture in the mind of the reader. Some of the verbs that describe the movement of the creature (e.g. *bestirred*, *floundered*, *slithered*) can be discussed, focusing on why the poet chose to use those specific ones. The poem itself has a regular verse and rhyme pattern.

The interplay between the powerful theme and narrative and the humour means that pupils can read with expression to illustrate the meaning they have inferred.

LINKS TO WHOLE-CLASS WORK

This is an exemplar that should follow whole-class work based around similar learning objectives. Pupils in Year 4 will have been looking at a number of different poems as a class, identifying common themes, as well as looking at structural features such as rhyme and verse patterns. Teachers will have modelled how these patterns can be utilised when reading aloud effectively and using intonation to indicate the speaker's interpretation and response to the poem. Pupils will then have done the same independently and in guided groups.

The following exemplar illustrates how a guided group might focus on another poem in the same way. This guided session could occur alongside the whole-class teaching session but also take place some time afterwards.

TEXT INTRODUCTION

Children are encouraged to identify the text type and introduce the text to themselves.

Teacher:
- Asks pupils to look carefully at the poem. What do you notice about it?
- Prompts pupils if needed, e.g. Look at the layout of the stanzas and rhyme pattern.

STRATEGY CHECK

Teacher:
- Identifies some of the unusual vocabulary and discusses potential meaning.

  What does bestirred mean? How can we read around the word to help us make a good guess? What about *lurch, floundered, reeled*?

- Models reading first stanza.

  Let me read the first stanza to you. Listen to how reading the lines of a poem uses a different rhythm than reading a story. Listen to the expression that I use and try to do the same when you are reading.

- Directs pupils' attention to the meaning of the poem by asking children to keep the following questions in mind.

  What is the Malfeasance?
  What happens to the Malfeasance?
  What lessons is the poet trying to teach us in this poem?

INDEPENDENT READING

Each child works with their own copy of the poem.

During reading the teacher:
- observes, prompts and praises. Teacher particularly listens to how children read the poem aloud effectively, e.g. I really liked that way you emphasised the alliteration in the line 'bullets bounced off the beast', well done.
- Prompts and checks for meaning of specific vocabulary.

RETURNING TO THE TEXT

- The teacher works with the group on specific teaching points.

  I really liked the way you read the last stanza, can you read it again to the group and we'll all listen to how you varied the volume of your voice and use of rhythm to good effect.

  What did you think the Malfeasance was?
  What words helped you to make that judgement?

INDEPENDENT ACTIVITY/FURTHER READING

Pupils prepare in pairs to read the poem aloud to the class during the plenary.

THE MALFEASANCE

It was dark, dark, dreadful night
And while millions were abed
The Malfeasance bestirred itself
And raised its ugly head.

The leaves dropped quietly in the night
In the sky Orion shone;
The Malfeasance bestirred itself
Then crawled around till dawn.

Taller than a chimney stack,
More massive than a church,
It slithered to the city
With a purpose and a lurch.

Squelch, squelch, the scaly feet
Flapped along the roads;
Nothing like it had been seen
Since a recent fall of toads.

Bullets bounced off the beast,
Aircraft made it grin,
Its open mouth made an eerie sound
Uglier than sin.

Still it floundered forwards,
Still the city reeled;
There was panic on the pavements,
Even policemen squealed.

Then suddenly someone suggested
(As the beast had done no harm)
It would be kinder to show it kindness
Better to stop the alarm.

When they offered it refreshment
The creature stopped in its track;
When they waved a greeting to it
Steam rose from its back.

As the friendliness grew firmer
The problem was quietly solved:
Terror turned to triumph and
The Malfeasance dissolved.

And where it stood there hung a mist,
And in its wake a shining trail,
And the people found each other
And thereby hangs a tail.

Alan Bold

YEAR 4 BOOK LIST	Author/Editor	Publisher/Date	ISBN
FICTION			
A Walk with Granny	Nigel Grey	Cambridge Reading Scheme 1998	0521469287
Animal Heroes	C. Warren and Judy Waite	Literacy World /Heinemann 2000	0435117149 (Pack of 6)
Ask Einstein!	Alan Trussell-Cullen	Redcliffe Publishing 1999	0478245769
Beaten By A Balloon	Margaret Mahy	Puffin 1999	0140562826
Beauty and the Beast	Tessa Krailing	Scholastic Hippo 2001	0439997518
Beaver Towers	Nigel Hinton	Puffin (new edn) 1995	0140370609
Beware!	Pauline Cartwright	Redcliffe Publishing 1999	0478245777
Bill's New Frock	Anne Fine	Mammoth 1990	0749703059
BJ Goes on Holiday	Stan Cullimore, Wendy Body (ed.)	Longman Book Project (Longman) 1994	0582122201
Blessu and Dumpling	Dick King-Smith	Puffin 1992	0140346988
Bug Brother	Pete Johnson	Puffin 2000	0141307420
Centuries of Stories	Wendy Cooling (ed.)	HarperCollins 1999	0006754155
Cliffhanger	Jacqueline Wilson	Yearling 1995	0440863384
Conker	Michael Morpurgo	Mammoth 1998	0749733764
Dinosaurs And All That Rubbish	Michael Foreman	Puffin 1993	014055260X
Double Switch	Diana Noonan	Redcliffe Publishing 1999	0478245823
Fair's Fair	Leon Garfield	Hodder Wayland 2001	0340795220
Fairy Tales	Terry Jones	Puffin 1990	0140322620
Freckle Juice	Judy Blume	Macmillan 2001	0330308297
Gerbil Crazy	Tony Bradman	Puffin 1991	0140341307
Gracie	Carolyn Sloan, Wendy Body (ed.)	Longman Book Project (Longman) 1994	0582122155
Haddock	Jan Mark	Simon & Schuster Young Books 1994	0750014458
Hamburger Heaven	Wong Herbert Yee	Houghton Mifflin Company 1999	039587548X
Hang in There, Oscar Martin!	Diana Noonan	Redcliffe Publishing 1999	0478245858
Horrid Henry And The Secret Club	Francesca Simon	Orion 1996	1858812925
Horse Pie	Dick King-Smith	Young Corgi 1994	0552527858
How I Met Archie	Anna Kenna	Redcliffe Publishing 1999	0478245866
Ishtar And Tammuz	Christopher Moore	Francis Lincoln 1997	0711210993
It was a Dark and Stormy Night	Allan Ahlberg, Janet Ahlberg (illus.)	Puffin 1998	0141300272
It's Too Frightening For Me	Shirley Hughes	Puffin 1986	0140320083
Jeremiah in the Dark Woods	Allan Ahlberg	Puffin 1999	0141304960
Keep it Clean	David Webb, Wendy Body (ed.)	Longman Book Project (Longman) 1994	0582122260
King Herla's Ride	Jan Mark	Scholastic Hippo 2000	0439996112
Leaving the Island	Judith O'Neill	Cambridge Reading Scheme 1998	0521637457
Little Red Cap	Jacob Grimm et al. (eds)	North South Books 1995	1558584307
M.O.L.E (Much Overworked Little Earthmover)	Russell Hoban and Jan Pienkowski	Red Fox (Jonathan Cape) 1993	0224030612
Matt's Million	Andrew Norriss	Puffin 1996	014036899X
Mossycoat	Philip Pullman	Hippo Books 1998	059054392X
Mufaro's Beautiful Daughters	John Steptoe	Puffin 1997	0140559469
Musicians of Bremen	Ann Jungman	Scholastic Hippo 2001	0439997577
Never Hitch a Ride with a Martian	Tony Clark	Redcliffe Publishing 1999	0478245904
Pidge	Krista Bell and Ann James	Little Ark Books 1997	1864483601
Pippi Longstocking	Astrid Lindgren	Puffin 1996	0140379096
Psyche And Eros	Marcia Williams	Cambridge 1998	0521477867
School Trouble	Narinda Dhami	Literacy World /Heinemann 1998	0435117165 (Pack of 6)
Scrapman	Carolyn Bear	Oxford Reading Tree, OUP 1999	0199186839
Sink the Gizmo	Paul Jennings	Puffin 1998	0140381481
Sunshine Island, Moonshine Baby	Clare Cherrington	HarperCollins	0261664859
The Conker as Hard as a Diamond	Chris Powling	Puffin 1985	0140317171
The Dad Library	Dennis Wheleham	Corgi 1997	0552529796
The Finders	Nigel Hinton	Puffin 1994	0140362398
The Great Piratical Rumbustification	Margaret Mahy	Puffin 1981	0140312617
The Great Time Warp Adventure	Jon Scieszka	Penguin 1996	0146003225

YEAR 4 BOOK LIST	Author/Editor	Publisher/Date	ISBN
The Guard Dog	Dick King-Smith	Young Corgi 1992	0552527319
The Hagstone	David Oakden	Anglia Young Books 2001	1871173612
The Happy Prince	Jane Ray	Orchard 1996	1860390927
The Iliad & The Odyssey	Marcia Williams	Walker 1998	0744554306
The Iron Man	Ted Hughes	Faber 1989	0571141498
The Last Wolf	Ann Turnbull	Penguin 1999	0140553045
The Little Mermaid	Linda Newbery	Scholastic Hippo 2001	0439997585
The Magic Finger	Roald Dahl	Puffin 1996	0140371583
The Man Whose Mother Was A Pirate	Margaret Mahy	Puffin 1996	0140554300
The Owl Tree	Jenny Nimmo	Walker 1997	0744554004
The Pedlar of Swaffham	Philippa Pearce	Scholastic Hippo 2001	0439999235
The Phantom Knicker Nicker	Jean Ure	Puffin 1995	0140374647
The Roman Beanfeast	Gillian Cross, Linzi Henry (illus.)	Puffin 1997	0140377662
The Tale of Greyfriars Bobby	Lavinia Derwent	Puffin 1985	0140311815
The Tale Of The Terrible Teeth	Hazel Townson	Mammoth 1998	0749735090
The Thief's Daughter	Alan Marks	MacDonald 1993	0750013788
The Ugly Duckling	Helen Dunmore	Scholastic Hippo 2001	0439999227
There's A Troll At The Bottom Of My Garden	Ann Jungman	Puffin 1993	0140344748
Tristars (Series)		Horwitz-Martin	
Who's for the Zoo?	Jean Ure, Wendy Body (ed.)	Longman Book Project (Longman) 1994	0582122120
NON-FICTION			
A Family in the Thirties	Sue Crawford	Wayland 1988	1852106042
Alice's Diary	Marie Gibson	Redcliffe Publishing 2000	0478245750
All Kinds of Places to Live	Susan Thomas	Oxford Reading Tree (Oxford) 1995	0199167001
Amazing Places to Live	Nick Middleton	Oxford Reading Tree (Oxford) 1995	0199167052
Amazing Poisonous Animals	Alexandra Parsons	Dorling Kindersley (US) 1997	8421613820
Bungy 70528	Nic Bishop	Skyrider (Lioncrest) (Aus.)	0478229291
Canoe Diary	Nic Bishop	Skyrider (Lioncrest) (Aus.)	0478230745
Caught in a Flash	Nic Bishop	Skyrider (Lioncrest) (Aus.)	047822950X
Deadly and Dangerous Snakes	Ted Mertens	Magic Bean (Rigby) 1999	1863742247
Dear Sam, Dear Ben	Josephine Croser	Magic Bean (Rigby) 1998	0435045202
Different Jobs in Different Places	Susan Thomas	Oxford Reading Tree (Oxford) 1995	0199167036
Exploring Where You Live	Terry Jennings	Oxford Reading Tree (Oxford) 1995	0199167044
Family Life in Victorian Britain	Richard Wood	Wayland 1994	0750223049
Festivals	Jo Ely	Longman 1998	0582334217 (Pack of 6)
Fifty Years Ago: At Home	Karen Bryant-Mole	Wayland 1998	0750223936
Fifty Years Ago: In the High Street	Karen Bryant-Mole	Wayland 1998	0750225793
For and Against	Jenny Alexander	Pelican Longman 2000	0582344913
Frogs and Other Amphibians	James Frances	Folens 1999	1841632864
Helen Keller	Nina Morgan	Wayland 1995	075021676X
How We Used to Live: Victorians Early & Late	David Evans	A & C Black 1990	0713633107
I Wonder Why Snakes Shed Their Skins?	Amanda O'Neill	Kingfisher 1996	1856976696
Journeys (series)	Karen Bryant-Mole	A & C Black	
Life in Space	David Glover	Literacy World /Heinemann 1998	0435096591
Making Tracks	Steve Parker	Walker 1998	0744554136
Mountain Bike Challenge	Patrick Morgan	Redcliffe Publishing 2000	0478245890
Natural Record Breakers	Jillian Powell	Literacy World /Heinemann 1998	0435096656
Night Lights	Hill *et al.*	Redcliffe Publishing 2000	0478245912
Roald Dahl	Andrea Shavick	Oxford 1997	0199104409
Rocking & Rolling	Philip Steale	Walker 1997	0744528909
Rome and Romans	Heather Amery, Patricia Vanagas	Usborne Publishing Ltd 1997	0746030711
Round the World Cookbook	Jane Asher	Longman Book Project (Longman) 1994	0582122805
School by a Volcano	Bobby Neate (ed.)	Longman Book Project (Longman) 1994	0582123143
Searching for Sea Lions	Kim Westerskov	Redcliffe Publishing 1999	0478245947
Sky Rider	Andy and Angie Belcher	Learning Media (Aus.) 1999	0478231121

YEAR 4 BOOK LIST	Author/Editor	Publisher/Date	ISBN
Spacebusters: The Race To The Moon	Philip Wilkinson	Dorling Kindersley 1998	0751357367
The Living Rainforest	Nic Bishop	Redcliffe Publishing 2000	0478245882
The Pebble In My Pocket	Meredith Hooper and Chris Coady	Lincoln 1996	0711210225
The Planets	Patrick Moore	Red Fox 1996	0099678918
The Roman Chronicle	John Barraclough	Literacy World /Heinemann 1998	0435096648 (Pack of 6)
The Sky's the Limit	Tony Christiansen	Redcliffe Publishing 1999	0478245955
A Town At Work	Valerie Fawcett	Oxford Reading Tree (Oxford) 1995	019916701X
Victorians	Clare Chandler	Wayland 1994	0750212675
Why Don't Ships Sink?	Jillian Powell	Pelican Longman 2000	0582346789
Wild Bird	Angie Belcher	Redcliffe Publishing 1998	047824598X
Zoos, Past and Present	Graham Meadows	Shortland Publications 1989	0868675547

Literacy consultants have also recommended the following sources for leaflets, which can also form the basis of guided reading sessions:

Sainsbury's Recipe Cards	Jamie Oliver		
World Wildlife Fund leaflet for Rhino Supporters			

POETRY

Alphabet Spook	Nicholas Tulloch, Chris Mould (illus.)	Oxford 1997	0192761560
Bad Bad Cats	Roger McGough	Puffin 1997	0140328246
Blackbird Has Spoken	Eleanor Farjeon, Anne Harvey (ed.)	Macmillan 1999	0330371843
Cat Among the Pigeons	Kit Wright	Puffin 1989	0140323678
Heard it in the Playground	Allan Ahlberg	Puffin 1991	0140328246
Golden Apples	Fiona Waters (ed.)	Macmillan 1999	0330297287
Paul Revere's Ride	Henry Wadsworth Longfellow, Ted Rand (illus.)	Dutton Children's Books 1996	0140556125
Sadderday and Funday	Andrew Fusek Peters	Hodder Wayland 2001	0750235500
Snollygoster	Helen Dunmore	Scholastic Hippo 2001	0439996368
Space Time Rhythm and Rhyme	Russell Stannard	Faber 1999	0571195792
Strawberry Drums	Adrian Mitchell, Frances Lloyd (illus.)	Macmillan 1998	0750003642
Talking Drums	Veronique Tadjo (ed.)	A & C Black 2001	0713658150
Teachers' Pets	Paul Cookson	Macmillan 1999	0330368680
The Blue and Green Ark	Brain Patten	Scholastic Hippo 1999	0590113895
The Jumblies	Edward Lear, Emily Bolan (illus.)	Doubleday 2001	0385601174
The World Is Sweet	Valerie Bloom	Bloomsbury 2001	0747551154
My Granny is a Sumo Wrestler	Gareth Owen	HarperCollins 1999	000674883X
Night and Day	Robert Louis Stevenson	*A Child's Garden of Verses*, Oxford 1966	0192760653
Quick Let's Get Out Of Here	Michael Rosen	Puffin 1999	0140317848
The Malfeasance	Alan Bold	*The Oxford Book of Story Poems*, Oxford 1999	0192762125
The Seal Hunter	Tony Mitton	Scholastic Hippo 1998	0590543903
The Red and White Spotted Handkerchief	Tony Mitton	Scholastic Hippo 2001	0439994071
Up On the Roof	Matthew Sweeney	Faber 2001	0571207286

MEDIA

Double Act	Jacqueline Wilson	Channel 4 Book Box	

MORE CHALLENGING LITERARY TEXTS FOR YEAR 4 PUPILS

A Child's Garden of Verses	Robert Louis Stevenson	Oxford 1966	0192760653
Charlotte's Web	E.B. White	Puffin 1969	0140301852
Godhanger	Dick King-Smith	Corgi 1997	0552545015
Hiawatha's Childhood	Henry Wadsworth Longfellow	Puffin 1986	0140505628
Juggling with Gerbils	Brian Patten	Puffin 2000	0141304782
Stuart Little	E.B. White	Puffin 2000	0141305061
The Better Brown Stories	Allan Ahlberg	Puffin 1996	0140373691
The Midnight Fox	Betsy Byers	Puffin 1976	014030844X
The Secret Friends	Elizabeth Laird	Hodder Children's Books 1997	0340664738

GUIDED READING

YEAR 5

TRADITIONAL TALE/ LEGEND

SIR GAWAIN AND THE GREEN KNIGHT
Retold by Selina Hastings

Walker Books (1987)

ISBN 0744520053

TEACHING FOCUS FOR TWO SESSIONS

- To identify the features of myths, legends and fables, e.g. the moral in a fable
- To identify the structure and themes of legends
- To make notes of story outline as a preparation for oral storytelling.

TEXT SELECTION NOTES

Sir Gawain and the Green Knight is an Arthurian legend retold by Selina Hastings.

As with most legends, the plot structure is very straightforward. There is a brief orientation or scene-setting paragraph, quickly followed by the problem: the Green Knight appears and challenges any knight to combat. The rules are that the knight can strike the first blow with an axe. Then in a year's time the knight must allow the Green Knight to return the blow.

Gawain accepts the challenge and slices off the head of the Green Knight. The Green Knight rises to his feet, picks up his head and gallops out of the hall.

The tale continues with Sir Gawain going in search of the Green Knight and undergoing a series of temptations as the plot moves towards its climax with the confrontation with the Green Knight. Final resolution is achieved and there is a brief coda as Gawain returns to Camelot and tells his story to the court.

The simplicity of the plot structure means that this is a good tale for pupils to analyse as well as to discuss the underlying theme based on the chivalry of the knights.

In addition, the skilful delineation and development of character by the author enables a focus upon the construction of characters to be a fruitful one.

LINK TO WHOLE-CLASS WORK

This guided reading session is most productive if it follows whole-class work on myths and legends and their features and themes. In particular, work around Selina Hastings' other retelling of an Arthurian legend *Sir Gawain and the Loathly Lady* (Walker Books) is recommended as the key text for shared reading.

SIR GAWAIN AND THE GREEN KNIGHT
SESSION 1

TEACHING OBJECTIVES (IN ADDITION TO OVERALL TEACHING OBJECTIVES)

- To identify use of incident, dialogue and action to give insights into the character of King Arthur.
- To practise silent reading.

TEXT INTRODUCTION AND STRATEGY CHECK

Teacher:
- Outlines teaching objectives.
- Prompts pupils to consider cover and title and predict what kind of text it is. Drawing on previous work on legends, pupils predict the features they are likely to encounter.

INDEPENDENT READING

Teacher:
- Sets pupils off with explicit instructions:

  Read silently to the end of page 9.
  Note down in your reading notebooks: an action and a piece of speech by King Arthur which give insights into his character.
- Listens to each child read aloud a short part as others read silently to check on use of searchlights.

RETURNING TO THE TEXT

Teacher:
- Asks pupils to give their judgements concerning King Arthur's character.
- Encourages pupils to cite which action and dialogue have led to their insights.
- You said that you think King Arthur is a clever and a brave man. What does he do or say to make you think that?

FOLLOW-UP INDEPENDENT WORK/ FURTHER READING

Teacher gives specific tasks to be completed before next guided reading session:

- Read the rest of the book.
- Identify and note down the key incidents in the story in your reading notebooks.
- Note down what the theme or moral of the story is in your reading notebooks.

SIR GAWAIN AND THE GREEN KNIGHT
SESSION 2

TEACHING OBJECTIVES

- To make notes of story outline as preparation for oral storytelling.
- To identify the structure and themes of legends.

INTRODUCTION (INCLUDING RETURNING TO THE TEXT)

Teacher:
- Reiterates learning objectives.
- Checks all pupils have read to the end of book and noted down main events of story.
- Leads discussion about moral/theme of story:

  What did you think the theme of the story was?
  What does Sir Gawain do to demonstrate that?
  Is the theme similar to one of the themes we identified when we looked at a range of myths and legends as a whole class?

INDEPENDENT ACTIVITY

Teacher:
- Sets pupils off on independent activity with explicit instructions. In pairs, take it in turns to tell each other the main events of the story.
- Supports each pair in deciding the main events. Pupils add or delete events where necessary. Teacher reminds them that these will be used as prompts for an oral retelling.

RETURNING TO THE TEXT

- Pupils as a group discuss any general issues e.g. main events v. minor events.
- Teacher reminds pupils of the techniques of oral storytelling, and explains who the audience will be (e.g. another pair, whole class, another class).

FOLLOW-UP INDEPENDENT TASK/ FURTHER READING

Pupils, in pairs, prepare an oral storytelling of Sir Gawain and the Green Knight.

The head rolled on the floor, blood spurting from the wound, but the Knight never faltered. Rising to his feet, he picked up his head and, tucking it under his arm, swung himself up into the saddle.

GUIDED READING

YEAR 5

NARRATIVE POEM

THE HIGHWAYMAN
Alfred Noyes

Illustrated by Charles Keeping

Oxford (1999)

ISBN 0192797484

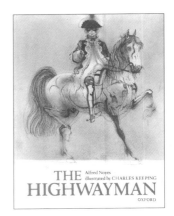

**TEACHING
OBJECTIVES**

- To read a range of narrative poems.
- To explore the appeal of older literature.
- To understand terms which describe different kinds of poems, e.g. ballad, sonnet, rap, elegy, narrative poem, and to identify particular features.
- To appreciate the differences between literal and figurative language, e.g. through discussing the effects of imagery in poetry.

**TEXT SELECTION
NOTES**

Alfred Noyes wrote 'The Highwayman' in 1913 and it is the poem for which he is best known. It was recently voted one of the nation's favourite poems in a BBC poll.

'The Highwayman' tells the story of Bess, the landlord's daughter and her love for the Highwayman. Soldiers arrive at the Tavern and use Bess as a hostage/decoy to entrap the Highwayman. Bess sacrifices her own life in order to warn the Highwayman. However, so incensed is he at hearing of her death that he charges back to confront the soldiers and also perishes. On moonlit nights the two lovers can still be observed meeting, their love strong enough to survive death. The power of the narrative engages children and carries them through the poem. This enables them to engage with the literary language, which is rich in simile and metaphor.

Noyes uses repetition effectively in both the repetition of stanzas, lines and phrases as well as sound, including rhyme and alliteration. Indeed the beginning of the poem is almost exactly the same as the ending.

'The Highwayman' is a wonderfully rich poem for teaching both as a whole-class text as well as for guided reading.

**LINK TO
WHOLE-CLASS WORK**

This work on narrative poetry is best completed after the class has considered some other narrative poems (e.g. 'The Lady of Shallot'). In so doing they will have considered a range of narrative poems and begun to consider older literature. In particular they will have been looking at figurative language, of which these poems are full of examples. It does take some time for pupils to understand the complexity of meanings that can be gleaned from metaphors in the poems. A line such as 'The moon was a ghostly galleon tossed upon cloudy seas' from 'The Highwayman' can give rise to intense thought and can form the basis of a whole Literacy Hour!

TEXT INTRODUCTION

Teacher:

- Introduces title and poet and type of poem:

  This is a narrative poem. What does that mean? What do you expect the poem to do? How are narrative poems different from other types/forms of poem? (e.g. limerick, cinquain, haiku). Tell me at least two ways in which they are different.

- Focuses pupils on to the figurative language:

  Read the first three lines. What do you notice? (e.g. repetitive structure, each line is a metaphor describing the setting and creating mood). Why has the poet used this figurative language and not just written 'The moon shone on the road. It was cloudy'?

- Asks pupils to read independently; and to consider the following.
  Identify any other metaphors in the poem and consider their effect; why are the last two stanzas written in italic?

INDEPENDENT READING

- Each pupil reads their own copy of the poem silently.
- During reading teacher observes, prompts and praises. Teacher intervenes to ask pupils if they have spotted any more figurative language, discusses any examples and their effect on meaning.

RETURNING TO THE TEXT

- The teacher works with the group on specific teaching points, for example:

  John spotted that the road is described as 'a gypsy's ribbon' in stanza 1 of part 2. Can you tell everyone what you thought the poet was trying to describe by changing the metaphor used to describe the road from the description in the first stanza?
  Can you explain why the last two stanzas are written in italic. Does everyone agree?

INDEPENDENT ACTIVITY/FURTHER READING

Pupils use the structure of the first three lines to construct their own descriptive metaphors to add to class 'figurative language bank'.

THE HIGHWAYMAN

The wind was a torrent of darkness among the gusty trees,
The moon was a ghostly galleon tossed upon cloudy seas.
The road was a ribbon of moonlight over the purple moor,
And the highwayman came riding—
      Riding— riding—
The highwayman came riding, up to the old inn-door.

He'd a French cocked-hat on his forehead, a bunch of lace at his chin,
A coat of claret velvet, and breeches of brown doe-skin.
They fitted with never a wrinkle. His boots were up to the thigh.
And he rode with a jewelled twinkle,
      His pistol butts a-twinkle,
His rapier hilt a-twinkle, under the jewelled sky.

Over the cobbles he clattered and clashed in the dark inn-yard.
He tapped with his whip on the shutters, but all was locked and barred.
He whistled a tune to the window, and who should be waiting there
But the landlord's black-eyed daughter,
      Bess, the landlord's daughter,
Plaiting a dark, red love-knot into her long black hair.

And dark in the dark old inn-yard a stable-wicket creaked
Where Tim the ostler listened. His face was white and peaked.
His eyes were hollows of madness, his hair like mouldy hay,
But he loved the landlord's daughter,
      The landlord's red-lipped daughter.
Dumb as a dog he listened, and he heard the robber say—

'One kiss, my bonny sweetheart, I'm after a prize to-night,
But I shall be back with the yellow gold before the morning light;
Yet, if they press me sharply, and harry me through the day,
Then look for me by moonlight,
      Watch for me by the moonlight,
I'll come to thee by moonlight, though hell should bar the way.'

He rose upright in the stirrups. He scarce could reach her hand,
But she loosened her hair i' the casement. His face burnt like a brand
As the black cascade of perfume came tumbling over his breast;
And he kissed its waves in the moonlight,
      (Oh, sweet black waves in the moonlight!)
Then he tugged at his rein in the moonlight, and galloped away to the west.

He did not come in the dawning.
He did not come at noon;
And out o' the tawny sunset, before the rise o' the moon,
When the road was a gipsy's ribbon, looping the purple moor,
A red-coat troop came marching—
     Marching—marching—
King George's men came marching, up to the old inn-door.

They said no word to the landlord. They drank his ale instead.
But they gagged his daughter, and bound her, to the foot of her narrow bed.
Two of them knelt at her casement, with muskets at their side!
There was death at every window;
     And hell at one dark window;
For Bess could see, through her casement, the road that he would ride.

They had tied her up to attention, with many a sniggering jest.
They had bound a musket beside her, with the muzzle beneath her breast!
'Now, keep good watch!' and they kissed her,
     She heard the dead man say—
Look for me by moonlight:
     Watch for me by moonlight:
I'll come to thee by moonlight, though hell should bar the way!

She twisted her hands behind her; but all the knots held good!
She writhed her hands till her fingers were wet with sweat or blood!
They stretched and strained in the darkness, and the hours crawled by like years,
Till, now, on the stroke of midnight,
     Cold, on the stroke of midnight,
The tip of one finger touched it! The trigger at least was hers!

The tip of one finger touched it. She strove no more for the rest.
Up, she stood up to attention, with the muzzle beneath her breast.
She would not risk their hearing; she would not strive again;
For the road lay bare in the moonlight;
     Blank and bare in the moonlight:
And the blood of her veins, in the moonlight, throbbed to her love's refrain.

Tlot-tlot; tlot-tlot! Had they heard it? The horse-hoofs ringing clear;
Tlot-tlot; tlot-tlot, in the distance! Were they deaf that they did not hear?
Down the ribbon of moonlight, over the brow of the hill,
The highwayman came riding, Riding, riding!
The red-coats looked to their priming! She stood up, straight and still.

Tlot-tlot, in the frosty silence! Tlot-tlot, in the echoing night!
Nearer he came and nearer. Her face was like a light.
Her eyes grew wide for a moment; she drew one last deep breath,
Then her finger moved in the moonlight,
        Her musket shattered the moonlight,
Shattered her breast in the moonlight and warned him— with her death.

He turned. He spurred to the west; he did not know who stood
Bowed, with her head o'er the musket, drenched with her own red blood!
Not till the dawn he heard it, and his face grew grey to hear
How Bess, the landlord's daughter,
        The landlord's black-eyed daughter,
Had watched for her love in the moonlight, and died in the darkness there.

Back, he spurred like a madman, shouting a curse to the sky,
With the white road smoking behind him and his rapier brandished high
Blood-red were his spurs i' the golden noon; wine-red was his velvet coat;
When they shot him down on the highway,
        Down like a dog on the highway,
And he lay in his blood on the highway, with the bunch of lace at his throat.

And still of a winter's night, they say, when the wind is in the trees,
When the moon is a ghostly galleon tossed upon cloudy seas,
When the road is a ribbon of moonlight over the purple moor,
A highwayman comes riding—
        Riding—riding—
A highwayman comes riding, up to the old inn-door.

Over the cobbles he clatters and clangs in the dark inn-yard.
And he taps with his whip on the shutters, but all is locked and barred.
He whistles a tune to the window, and who should be waiting there
But the landlord's black-eyed daughter,
        Bess, the landlord's daughter,
Plaiting a dark, red love-knot into her long black hair.

Alfred Noyes

A highwayman comes riding—
Riding—riding—
A highwayman comes riding, up to the old inn-door.

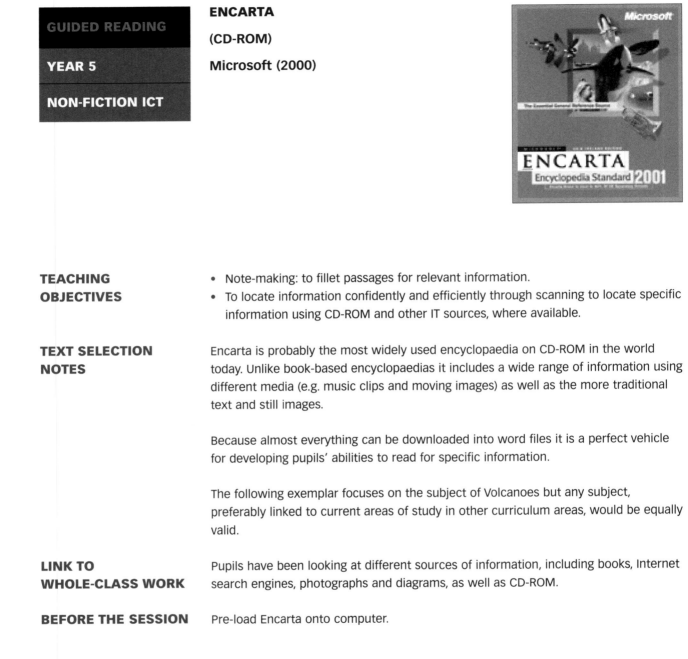

GUIDED READING

YEAR 5

NON-FICTION ICT

ENCARTA

(CD-ROM)

Microsoft (2000)

TEACHING OBJECTIVES

- Note-making: to fillet passages for relevant information.
- To locate information confidently and efficiently through scanning to locate specific information using CD-ROM and other IT sources, where available.

TEXT SELECTION NOTES

Encarta is probably the most widely used encyclopaedia on CD-ROM in the world today. Unlike book-based encyclopaedias it includes a wide range of information using different media (e.g. music clips and moving images) as well as the more traditional text and still images.

Because almost everything can be downloaded into word files it is a perfect vehicle for developing pupils' abilities to read for specific information.

The following exemplar focuses on the subject of Volcanoes but any subject, preferably linked to current areas of study in other curriculum areas, would be equally valid.

LINK TO WHOLE-CLASS WORK

Pupils have been looking at different sources of information, including books, Internet search engines, photographs and diagrams, as well as CD-ROM.

BEFORE THE SESSION

Pre-load Encarta onto computer.

TEXT INTRODUCTION

Teacher:
- Gathers group around computer monitor with Encarta pre-loaded.
- Discusses home page and draws from pupils the information that is available in each section.
- Clicks on 'Encyclopaedia articles'. Demonstrates how we could efficiently locate an article on the subject of volcanoes by using 'Pinpointers'.
- Downloads article on volcanoes.

STRATEGY CHECK

Teacher reminds pupils about how to scan for specific information using a key word (e.g. active) and then note or mark the relevant information.

INDEPENDENT READING

- Teacher sets a specific information focus for pupils to scan for and make notes, for example:

  I want you to note down five recently-active volcanoes and the last time they were active using the following table.

Name of Volcano	Location	Last Active Date

- Each pupil works with own copy of text on screen, or on hard copy if computer suite not available. Highlighter pens could be used for this activity if the pupils are working on hard copy, rather than tabulation.
- During the reading teacher observes, prompts and praises each child in turn, supporting pupils' scanning and note-making strategies.

RETURNING TO THE TEXT

- The teacher works with the group on specific teaching points:

  The way you used the highlighter was very efficient, Amir, would you show the others what you did and how it helped you with your scanning?

- Pupils share their findings.

LINK TO INDEPENDENT ACTIVITY/FURTHER READING

- Pupils use Encarta to search for relevant information about topics from other curriculum areas.
- Pupils use Encarta to search for a range of different sources in addition to text. These might be pictures, photographs and sound. In the article on Adolf Hitler, for example, there a number of photographs, a time-line and a recording of Hitler making a speech.

GUIDED READING

YEAR 5

NON-FICTION: INSTRUCTIONS (PROCEDURAL WRITING)

More challenging

REAL COOKING p.142
Nigel Slater

Penguin (1999)

ISBN 0140252770

CRAFTY ITALIAN COOKING p. 190
Michael Barry

Jarrold Publishing (1997)

ISBN 0711709629

These and other cookery books can be used to examine a range of pasta recipes.

TEACHING OBJECTIVES

- To read and evaluate a selection of recipes focusing on:
  - purpose
  - organisation and layout
  - clarity and usefulness.
- To extend the children's existing understanding of recipe writing through comparison focusing on the differences as well as the universal features.

TEXT SELECTION NOTES

The recipes selected should provide interesting contrasts. Although all the recipes mentioned in this exemplar ostensibly have the same purpose, there are subtle differences. Some might be browsed for pleasure and include food notes to interest the gourmet; others focus on the practicalities of food preparation. The challenge of this guided reading activity can be further increased by using different texts for comparison; there are innumerable pasta recipes in books, magazines, leaflets and packaging that can be used in this way.

Some important features of the texts selected for the following guided reading exemplar are as follows:

Nigel Slater is noted for his adoration of comfort food and this is reflected in the descriptions of the dishes.
- Headings emphasise links between food and emotions: *soothing, creamy pasta*.
- His pasta dish is 'Spicy, hot and creamy. A Pasta dish for a cold night.'
- Flavours and textures are emphasised: *sausage goo* at the bottom of the pan.
- Rough quantities for ingredients.
- Glossy photographs are used to emphasise the richness of the food.

Michael Barry's book presents quick and easy recipes, as reflected in the title *Crafty Italian*.

- Brief introductory notes provide some context: 'This dish with its patriotic three colours of the Italian flag twice repeated in the pasta and the dressing, is named after Italy's first queen.'
- Recipes are organised according to region: Naples, Calabria, Basilicata, Campagna.
- Recipes are clearly laid out on the page to facilitate easy reference during cooking.

LINKS TO WHOLE-CLASS WORK

This mixed Year 5/Year 6 class have revisited Instructional writing. In the introductory lesson with the whole class using Michael Barry's *Crafty Italian Cookery* the teacher assessed the children's prior experience and knowledge, and reinforced the pupils' knowledge of the features of instructional texts by compiling notes after the close study of a recipe from Michael Barry's book. These notes are on display and can be seen by the guided reading group. The notes contain the following outline which draws on the recipe:

- Goal: How to make *Pasta Margherita*, serves 4
- Materials/equipment needed: List of ingredients sometimes with preparation notes: *1 large pepper, seeded and cut into 5mm strips*
- Sequenced steps: *Cook the pasta, remove from the heat*
- Written in the present tense/imperative: *Cook the pasta, add the cheese*
- In chronological order: *Trim the spring onions **then** chop the white and cut the green ends*
- Impersonal address; no named individuals.

BEFORE THE GUIDED READING SESSION

In preparation for the guided reading session the children have been asked to independently read Nigel Slater's recipe for *Pasta with Spicy Sausage and Mustard*.

Resources required

- Large copy of Michael Barry's *Pasta Margherita* on the flipchart and the demonstration notes from the shared reading session for reference
- Six copies of Nigel Slater's *Pasta with Spicy Sausage and Mustard*
- A display of cookery books for reference
- Dictionaries to use as required

TEXT INTRODUCTION (INCLUDING RETURNING TO THE TEXT)

Teacher:
- Shows the front cover of the book and explains that Nigel Slater is a celebrity chef.
- Asks pupils to turn to page 142 and to look carefully at the copies of the recipe.
- Draws out **similarities** between the two examples (e.g. features of instructional texts listed above, organisation, layout)
- Shifts the discussion to focus on **differences**:
  Asks questions to get the children to consider ways in which this recipe is different from Michael Barry's, focusing on:

    descriptive colour provided by specific vocabulary used, e.g. *soothing, creamy, sausage goo, piping hot*

    words and phrases that link the food to **mood**, e.g. *Pasta for a cold night*

    the **photograph** of the dish, prompting pupils to list words to describe the food in the photograph.

- Insists that children extend their answers with justifications:

  Amy, can you give me two examples where the use of descriptive adjectives is different?

INDEPENDENT READING

Pupils in pairs note down further differences between the recipes. For example in the ingredients the quantities of olive oil and the type of pasta required by both recipes are expressed differently:

    Michael Barry *2 tbsp olive oil*
    Nigel Slater *Olive oil*
    Michael Barry *12 oz three-coloured spiral pasta shapes*
    Nigel Slater *4 handfuls of dried pasta (any tube or shell shape), about 250g*

RETURNING AND RESPONDING TO THE TEXT

Teacher:
- Asks pupils to outline any further differences they have found.
- Finishes by prompting pupils to discuss who would find the recipe useful:

  Who would be able to use this recipe? I'm not sure a beginner could, what do you think, Sabrina?
  Jamal, you said that reading this recipe didn't make you feel you wanted to cook it. Why was that? Who do you think this book was written for? Who would it appeal to?
  OK, to summarise: we think that the people who would find it most useful are people who already know how to cook quite well and who enjoy food and eating a lot.

INDEPENDENT ACTIVITY/FURTHER READING

- Children compare another chef's pasta recipe with Michael Barry's recipe

Or

- They suggest titles for recipes for a very hot day focusing on words to make the food irresistible.

Feedback from independent activity takes place in the plenary of the Literacy Hour. Emphasise how recipes contain basic structure but use language in different ways depending on the purpose and audience of the book.

YEAR 5 BOOK LIST	Author/Editor	Publisher/Date	ISBN
FICTION			
A Handful of Magic	Stephen Elboz	Oxford 2001	0192751344
A Land Without Magic	Stephen Elboz	Oxford 2001	0192718754
A Picture Book of Anne Frank	David Adler	Macmillan 1994	0330331922
A Treasury of Dragon Stories	Margaret Clark (ed.)	Kingfisher Books 1997	0753401363
Aquila	Andrew Norris	Puffin 1997	0140383654
Blabber Mouth	Morris Gleitzman	Macmillan 2001	033039777X
Blodin The Beast	Michael Morpurgo	Francis Lincoln 1996	0711209103
Castaways of the Flying Dutchman	Brian Jacques	Puffin 2002	0141312114
A Christmas Carol by Charles Dickens	adapted by Chris Mould	Oxford 1995	019272178X
Dark Secrets	Anthony Masters	Literacy World /Heinemann 1998	0435115413
Earth Magic, Sky Magic	Rosalind Kervin	Cambridge Reading Scheme 1999	052163525X
Harry Houdini – Wonderdog!	William Taylor	Redcliffe Publishing 1999	0478249063
Harry The Poisonous Centipede	Lynne Reid Banks	HarperCollins 1996	0001006843
Ice Palace	Robert Swindells	Puffin 1992	0140349669
Interrupting the Big Sleep	Janice Marriott	Redcliffe Publishing 1999	047824908X
Invasion of the Wire Ones	Laurence Staig, Wendy Body (ed.)	Longman Book Project (Longman) 1994	0582122368
Kasper in the Glitter	Philip Ridley, Chris Riddell (illus.)	Puffin 1995	0140368914
Keep Out	Fleur Beale	Redcliffe Publishing 1999	0478249098
Keeping Henry	Nina Bawden	Puffin 1989	014032805X
Lazy Bones Jones	Sheila Kelly Welch	Redcliffe Publishing 1999	047824911X
MacB	Neil Arksey	Puffin 1999	0141304154
Oliver Twist by Charles Dickens	adapted by Chris Mould	Oxford 1996	0192723146
One Thousand and One Arabian Nights	Geraldine McCaughrean	Oxford 1999	0192750135
Poor Me One	Grace Hallworth, Wendy Body (ed.)	Longman Book Project (Longman) 1995	0582122074
Rats!	Pat Hutchins	Red Fox 1991	0099931907
Scary Stories	Valerie Bierman (ed.)	Mammoth 1997	0749728353
Sir Gawain and the Green Knight	Selina Hastings	Walker 1987	0744520053
Sir Gawain and the Loathly Lady	Selina Hastings	Walker 1987	0744507804
Stickybeak	Morris Gleitzman	Macmillan 2001	0330397788
Stig of the Dump	Clive King	Puffin 1993	0140364501
Street Child	Berlie Doherty	Collins 1995	0006740200
Tales from India	J. E. B. Gray	Oxford 2001	0192751158
Tales of the Norse Gods	Barbara Leonie Picard	Oxford 2001	0192751166
The Battle of Bubble and Squeak	Philippa Pearce	Puffin 2000	0141307552
The Butterfly Lion	Michael Morpugo	HarperCollins 1996	0001006614
The Chilli Challenge and other Stories	N. Dhami, A. Barry and J. O'Neil	Literacy World /Heinemann 1998	0435115421
The Curse of Being Pharaoh	Janice Marriott	Redcliffe Publishing 1999	0478249020
The Dog I Share	Janice Marriott	Redcliffe Publishing 1999	0478249039
The Green Children	Kevin Crossley-Holland	Oxford 1997	0192723235
The Magic Lands	Kevin Crossley-Holland	Orion 2001	1842550519
The Man with No Shadow	Michael Rosen, Wendy Body (ed.)	Longman Book Project (Longman) 1994	0582122007
The Mousehole Cat	Antonia Barber	Walker 1993	0744523532
The Peacemaker		Literacy World /Heinemann 1999	0435116010 (Pack of 6)
The Puffin Twentieth Century Collection of Stories	Judith Elkin (ed.)	Viking Children's (Puffin) 1999	0670885231
The Slobberers	Paul Jennings and Morris Glergmann	Puffin 2000	0141310227
The Stinky Cheese Man	Jon Scieszka and Lane Smith	Puffin 1993	0140548963
There's A Pharaoh In our Bath	Jeremy Strong	Puffin 1997	0140375716
Thief!	Malorie Blackman	Corgi 1995	0552528080
Treasure Island	adapted by Chris Mould	Oxford 2001	0192725009
Very Best Friends	Robina Beckles Wilson	Literacy World /Heinemann 1998	043509341X
NON-FICTION			
A is for Africa	Ifeoma Onyefulu	Frances Lincoln 1996	0711210292
Amazing Clever Tricks		Lorenz Books 2000	0754802388
Ancient Egypt	James Mason	Longman 1999	0582337488

YEAR 5 BOOK LIST	Author/Editor	Publisher/Date	ISBN
Asli's Story	Adrienne Jansen	Redcliffe Publishing 2000	0478249462
Broomsticks and Balloons	Jenny Lachlan	Literacy World /Heinemann 1999	0435096753
Coastline Journey	Christine Butterworth	Ginn 1995	0602266378
Extracts from Zlata's Diary	Zlata Filipovic	Literacy World /Heinemann 1999	0435096710
Finding Your Way	John Bonallack	Redcliffe Publishing 2000	0478124047
Free Fall	Pat Quinn	Redcliffe Publishing 1999	0478249055
Funfax, Beginners Guide to Magic		Henderson	1855970465
How to Persuade People	Rob Alcraft	Literacy World /Heinemann 1999	043509677X
I Wonder Why Zips Have Teeth	Barbara Taylor	Kingfisher 1996	1856973301
Issues series		Magic Bean (Heinemann)	
It's a Frog's Life	Kate Murdoch and Stephen Ray	Literacy Links (Kingscourt) 1995	0732715482
Let me Persuade You…	S. Hoare and E. Morcom	Pelican Longman 1998	0582433479
News Flash!	Sharon Hill	Redcliffe Publishing 2000	0478249136
NEWSTIME	Northcliffe Newspapers (subscription only)		
Our Changing Earth	Angie Belcher	Redcliffe Publishing 2000	0478249144
Phenomenon series		Horwitz Martin Education	
Science Dictionary	David Glover	Heinemann 1997	0435094556
Simply Magic	Dominic Wood	Red Fox 2001	0099413965
Stars and Planets	Alistair Smith	Usborne 1998	0746035241
The Comet Of Doom	Andrew Donkin	Macdonald 1998	0750025336
The How, What & Why of Mammals	Gareth Coleman	Literacy World /Heinemann 1999	0435096737
Viewpoints on Waste	Rodney Martin	Magic Bean (Heinemann)	1863740538
Whale Tales	Kim Westerskov	Redcliffe Publishing 1999	0478249209
Wolves	Buck Wilde	Literacy Links (Kingscourt)	1572571268
POETRY			
All Night Café	Philip Gross	Faber 1993	0571167535
Cautionary Verses	Hilaire Belloc, Quentin Blake (illus.)	Red Fox 1995	0099295318
Charles Causley: Collected Poems for Children	Charles Causley, John Lawrence (illus.)	Macmillan 2000	0330389807
By St. Thomas Water	Charles Causley	*The Oxford Book of Story Poems* 1999	0192762125
Hiawatha	Henry Wadsworth Longfellow	Everyman 1993	0460872680
Jabberwocky	Lewis Carroll	*The Oxford Book of Story Poems* 1999	0192762125
Jonah and the Whale	Gareth Owen	*The Oxford Book of Story Poems* 1999	0192762125
Upon Westminster Bridge	William Wordsworth	*A Puffin Book of Verse* 1953	0140300724
Sir Patrick Spens	Anon.	*The Oxford Book of Story Poems* 1999	0192762125
Can I Buy a Slice of Sky	Grace Nichols (ed.)	Hodder Wayland 1993	0340588284
Classic Narrative Poems	Wendy Body (ed.)	Longman 2000	0582433282
Plum	Tony Mitton	Scholastic Hippo 1998	0590542915
Poems for 10 Year Olds	Susan Gibbs (ed.)	Macmillan 2000	0330392093
Swings and Shadows	Anne Harvey (ed.)	Red Fox 2001	0099646811
The Highwayman	Alfred Noyes	*The Oxford Book of Story Poems* 1999	0192762125
The Hypnotiser	Michael Rosen	Scholastic Hippo 1998	0590543423
The Illustrated Old Possum	T. S. Eliot	Faber 1976	0571105580
The Inchcape Rock	Robert Southey	*The Oxford Book of Story Poems* 1999	0192762125
The Listeners	Walter de la Mare	*The Oxford Book of Story Poems* 1999	0192762125
The Oxford Book of Story Poems	M. Harrison and C. Stuart-Clark (eds)	Oxford 1999	0192762125
The Pied Piper Of Hamelin	Robert Browning	Orchard 1994	1852136510
The Thirteen Secrets of Poetry	Adrian Mitchell	Hodder Wayland 1993	075001380X
Young Hippo Spooky Poems	Jennifer Curry (ed.)	Scholastic Hippo 1998	0590191713
MEDIA/ICT			
Encarta		Microsoft CD-ROM 2000	
Film & Literacy: Part 1 and Part 2	Julie Roberts	Film Education 1998	
Screening Stories Pack	Julie Roberts	Film Education	
Junior Newswise resources: www.dialogueworks.co.uk			
MORE CHALLENGING LITERARY TEXTS FOR YEAR 5 PUPILS			
101 Dalmatians	Dodie Smith	Heinemann 1956	0330243756

YEAR 5 BOOK LIST	Author/Editor	Publisher/Date	ISBN
Arthur: The Seeing Stone	Kevin Crossley-Holland	Orion 2001	0752844296
Five Children and It	E. Nesbit	Puffin 1984	0140367357
Floodland	Marcus Sedgewick	Dolphin 2000	1858817633
How To Live Forever	Colin Thompson	Red Fox 1998	0099461811
Moondial	Helen Cresswell	Puffin 1994	0140325239
Mrs Frisby and the Rats of Nimh	Robert C. O'Brien	Puffin 1975	0140307257
Shakespeare Stories	Leon Garfield	Puffin 1997	0140389385
The Banana Tree	James Berry	*The Oxford Book of Children's Stories* – Oxford (new ed.) 2001	0192801899
The Chicken Gave it to Me	Ann Fine	Mammoth 1993	0749714778
The Lady Of Shallot	Alfred, Lord Tennyson	*The Oxford Book of Story Poems* 1999	0192762125
The Lion, the Witch and the Wardrobe	C. S. Lewis	Collins (new ed.) 2000	0006716873
The Lives of Christopher Chant	Diana Wynne Jones	Collins (new ed.) 2000	0006755186
The Peppermint Pig	Nina Bawden	Puffin (new ed.) 1998	0140379118
The Wind in the Willows	Kenneth Grahame	Penguin 1994	0140621229
Water Wings	Morris Gleitzman	Macmillan 2001	0330398253

<table>
<tr><td>

GUIDED READING

YEAR 6

NON-FICTION: PUBLIC INFORMATION DOCUMENT

</td></tr>
</table>

ROAD CODE: A HIGHWAY CODE WRITTEN FOR YOUNGER ROAD USERS

The Department of the Environment, Transport and the Regions

Her Majesty's Stationery Office (1999)

ISBN 0115521771

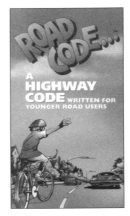 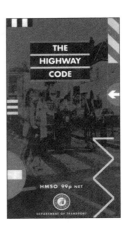

It would also be useful to have available *The Highway Code*. The Stationery Office ISBN 0115519777.

TEACHING OBJECTIVES

- To read and understand examples of official publications and their characteristic features, e.g. through discussion to consider information, legal documents, layout, use of footnotes, instructions, parenthesis, headings, appendices and asterisks.
- To understand features of formal official language through, for example:
    collecting and analysing examples, discussing when and why they are used;
    noting the conventions of the language, e.g. use of the impersonal voice, imperative verbs, formal vocabulary;
    collecting typical words and expressions, e.g. 'those wishing to …', 'hereby', 'forms may be obtained'.

TEXT SELECTION NOTES

Road Code was selected because it is an official document that has relevance to all children. Their own experience of being road users is addressed explicitly.

The text itself it clearly laid out in well-defined sections (e.g. *Pedestrians*, *Cyclists*, *Being a passenger*, etc.) Sentences are terse and to the point. The imperative tense is frequently used, for example on p. 6:

> **Don't show off when you are riding your bike on the road.**

There is good use of illustrations and a variety of fonts, print size and colour to create effect and emphasise certain key bits of advice.

LINKS TO WHOLE-CLASS WORK

In the whole-class teaching parts of the Literacy Hour, pupils have been looking at a range of public information documents – safety at swimming pools, the school prospectus, questionnaires, etc. – and examining their characteristic features. They will also be writing their own information document containing advice on what to do when visiting the local nature reserve.

TEXT INTRODUCTION

Teacher:

- Outlines learning objectives.
- Distributes text to individuals and asks them to skim read/flick through the text.
- Asks them to identify the text type and the function of this particular text.
- After one or two minutes asks a pupil to introduce the text to the group.
- Asks others if they wish to add anything.
- Tells pupils they will be reading independently a section of the text. As they read they will identify the focus for their section, any conventions of the language they notice (e.g. some examples of imperative verbs), as well as collecting one or two examples of typical words and sentence structure (e.g. 'if there is a footpath, use it').
- Tells pupils to also write down the different sources of information that the text uses (e.g. words, graphics, pictures) and how the most important information is highlighted and emphasised (e.g. capital letters, red print, boxes, use of illustrations with ticks and crosses).
- Gives each group member different sections to read (see contents page).

INDEPENDENT READING

- Pupils read and note down the characteristic features they identify in their section.
- Teacher supports each pupil in turn asking questions to help identify the features and to articulate the sources of information, for example:

Well done, you have noticed that this page does not contain instructions like most of the rest of the text. What function does this page have? Why do you think it has been included? What are the main points on this page?

RETURNING TO THE TEXT

- Pupils share the features they have noted and read out examples.
- As a group they list the different ways of emphasising and organising information.
- Teacher asks group to summarise their findings in a short oral report.

FOLLOW-UP INDEPENDENT WORK/ FURTHER READING

This could involve:

- Comparing *Road Code* to the full *Highway Code* and noting the differences in content and language features.
- Using the language and layout features of *Road Code* as a model for their own information document.
- Completing the word search on page 29 in *Road Code*.

GUIDED READING

YEAR 6

NON-FICTION: BIOGRAPHY AND AUTOBIOGRAPHY

BENJAMIN ZEPHANIAH
Verna Wilkins

Tamarind (1999)

ISBN 1870516389

OUT OF INDIA: AN ANGLO-INDIAN CHILDHOOD
Jamila Gavin

Hodder Children's Books (1997)

ISBN 0340854626

TEACHING OBJECTIVES	• To distinguish between biography and autobiography • To recognise the effect on the reader of the choice between first and third person • To distinguish between fact, opinion and fiction • To distinguish between implicit and explicit points of view and how these can differ.
TEXT SELECTION NOTES	Verna Wilkins' profile of poet Benjamin Zephaniah is a retelling based on several in-depth interviews with him. It is a short profile that can be read in a series of readings in one week. It is written as a narrative and includes a lot of direct speech. Jamila Gavin's story of her Anglo-Indian childhood combines personal recollection with an account of the achievement of Indian independence.
LINKS TO WHOLE-CLASS WORK	The class are familiar with Benjamin Zephaniah's poetry, having read and enjoyed *Talking Turkeys* as performance poetry. An author display of Jamila Gavin's fiction and other resources has been set up in the class library. Previously the class teacher has read *Benjamin Zephaniah* to the class.
Biography	• In shared reading the teacher has demonstrated the construction of a writing frame for this genre of non-fiction, and has introduced the term biography. • In shared writing the pupils have designed interviews which have been carried out independently at home and they have gathered photographic evidence. • In guided writing the teacher has helped pupils to select information to include in a biography which they have written independently as an extended piece of writing.
Autobiography	In shared reading autobiographical writing has been introduced through using an extract from *Cider with Rosie* describing Laurie Lee's first day at school.

BIOGRAPHY AND AUTOBIOGRAPHY
SESSION 1

In this guided reading session the teacher wants to consolidate the children's understanding of biographical writing and introduce autobiographical writing, making the differences explicit.

* The teacher has asked the group to read chapter 2 of *Out of India* in preparation for the guided reading session.

TEXT INTRODUCTION

Teacher:
* Asks for general impressions about Jamila Gavin, prompting pupils to give a reason for their ideas, drawing on evidence in chapter 2.
* Reminds the group of the conventions of biographical writing referring to notes made during shared writing, on the flipchart.
* Asks for any differences between the book about Zephaniah and Gavin, referring to the term **autobiographical**.
 (NB *auto* is a prefix which means self; ask for suggestions for other words that begin with the prefix *auto* and look for the connection with self, e.g. autograph, automatic.)

INDEPENDENT READING

Teacher:
* Asks pupils to read from p. 24 from 'So here we lived' to the bottom of p. 25. As they read they should be paying attention to the ways in which the text is written, drawing on their work as a whole class.

RETURNING TO THE TEXT

Pupils read aloud from p. 24 'So here we lived' to the bottom of p. 25. The teacher prompts them to consider some of the conventions of autobiographical writing, suggesting that they think about the language structure and content. For example:

* **First-person narration:** *So here we lived for the next six years of my life*.
* **Feelings emphasised:** *I envied my brother*.
* **Reflective comment:** *Maybe it was to keep up with my brother, and earn his respect, that I was game for anything*. The teacher asks the pupils to consider whether Jamila thought this at the time or whether this is the adult author's point of view.
* **Significant events:** *Once he was swimming in the tank, I just jumped in too and promptly sank to the bottom because I hadn't yet learned*. The teacher asks the children to consider whether an autobiography has to include all the events in a person's life. Autobiography would be dull to read if every event was recounted. Writers recall what was significant either personally or historically.
* **Significant people:** Jamila writes about her feelings for her mother and brother in this extract.
* **Narrated like a story with temporal connectives:** *so here we lived*; *while I was learning to walk*; *long after I had tired of hide and seek*; *Once*, etc.

INDEPENDENT ACTIVITY/FURTHER READING

Teacher asks the group to read chapter 3 independently in preparation for the next guided reading session.

BIOGRAPHY AND AUTOBIOGRAPHY
SESSION 2

TEACHING OBJECTIVE

To distinguish between fact, opinion and fiction in autobiographical writing.

INTRODUCTION (INCLUDING RESPONDING TO THE TEXT)

Teacher:
- Asks pupils to reflect on chapter 3, for example:

  Did Jamila's experiences remind you of anything that has happened to you?

- Prompts some pupils to tell some anecdotes from personal experience.
- Asks the tellers to consider how they might have changed or elaborated their stories, written in a shared writing session, to make them more interesting.
- Moves on to helping pupils begin to distinguish between fact and opinion, reading the paragraph that begins on page 34.

FACT	OPINION
I suffered from chilblains	England was a shock
Gas stoves	I expected the streets to be paved with gold
	London was grey and bleak and drab

INDEPENDENT READING

Teacher:
- Asks pupils in their reading notebooks to identify some facts and opinions in the chapter (this can be a paired or an individual activity).
- Supports each pair in distinguishing between fact and opinion, and justifying their decision: Explain why you think that is opinion.

RETURNING TO THE TEXT

- Teacher asks what children think they have learnt from the guided reading session.

  What have we learnt about autobiographical writing? Are there any similarities with biography? Are there any important differences?

GUIDED READING

YEAR 6

LONGER NOVEL

TOM'S MIDNIGHT GARDEN
Three guided reading exemplars for Year 6

The next three exemplars are all based on versions of *Tom's Midnight Garden*. We wish to demonstrate here how one text can be used in a variety of different ways.

The first exemplar outlines how the whole text can be utilised by one guided reading group over an extended period of time (probably 6–8 weeks or so) independently of whatever else is going on within the whole class.

The second exemplar outlines how an extract from the novel can be utilised in a 'one-off' guided session, in the context of the whole class working on the novel in the Literacy Hour over a two-week period.

The third exemplar outlines how a film adaptation of *Tom's Midnight Garden* could be used as the basis for guided reading, although it again assumes that the children have had some experience of reading the novel itself.

GUIDED READING

YEAR 6

LONGER NOVEL WHOLE TEXT

TOM'S MIDNIGHT GARDEN
Philippa Pearce

Puffin (2000)

ISBN 0141300663

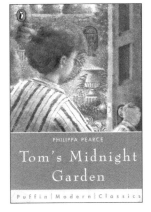

TEACHING OBJECTIVES COVERED OVER THE FOUR SESSIONS

- To understand aspects of narrative structure, e.g.
    how chapters in a book are linked together;
    how authors handle time (e.g. flashbacks, stories within stories, dreams);
    how the passing of time is conveyed to the reader.
- To annotate passages in detail in response to specific questions.
- To use a reading notebook or journal effectively to raise and refine personal responses to a text and prepare for discussion.
- To write a brief synopsis of a text, e.g. for a back cover blurb.

TEXT SELECTION NOTES

Tom's Midnight Garden by Philippa Pearce was first published in 1958. It is arguably one of the greatest works of children's literature to be written in the second half of the twentieth century and certainly deserves the accolade of 'classic'. In fact it might be regarded as a paradigmatic text of the post-war period, representing a shift from the rural to urban landscape of childhood.

Crucial to the story is the way that time is handled by the author in order that Tom, a boy living in the present, can spend time with Hatty, a girl who lived over half a century earlier. The novel is challenging in a number of ways, in addition to the above. First, it is a long novel, over 200 pages, and this requires sustained and concentrated reading over a period of time. Second, the 'present' of the book is now nearly half a century old and many details of daily life are different. Third, the relationship between Tom and Hatty, which is at the heart of the narrative, develops subtly; pupils need to be perceptive in understanding how that development is indicated through hints by the author as well as the action and dialogue that occurs within the text.

FURTHER POINTS
Setting

Contrasts post-war urbanisation with rural and idyllic Victorian setting.

Themes

Times, dreams, growing up.

Style

- Particularly when describing the garden, the prose is rhythmic and poetic.
- Colloquial in representing the intimate exchanges between Tom and Hatty.

Narrative Structure

- Home–away–home
- Time-slip

LINKS TO WHOLE-CLASS WORK

Pupils will have looked at other 'classics' of children's literature in Year 6 Term 1. This sequence of guided reading sessions suggests another way that a guided group could engage with a 'classic' children's novel.

TOM'S MIDNIGHT GARDEN
WHOLE TEXT: SESSION 1

INDEPENDENT PREPARATION FOR GUIDED READING

Each member of the guided group has been given a copy of the text. The pupils were asked to:
- read up to chapter 2;
- record in their reading notebooks their thoughts concerning:
    How Tom feels about having to stay with his aunt and uncle;
    Why he decided to write to Peter, who could not reply.

TEACHING OBJECTIVES

(See also the overall teaching objectives for the four sessions on p. 112.)
- Developing pupils' ability to make inferences about the text and to provide evidence for their opinion.

TEXT INTRODUCTION (INCLUDING RESPONDING TO THE TEXT)

Teacher:
- Asks a pupil to introduce the book to the rest of the group. Asks others if they wish to add anything.
- Discusses the pre-set questions, developing pupils' inferential abilities by asking them for evidence in the text to support their ideas, for example:

    If you think that Tom does not want Peter to reply because his aunt and uncle might discover how he truly felt about them, what does he say or do which reveals what he does actually think about his aunt and uncle?

- Gets pupils to look at the beginning of chapter 3 'By moonlight'.
- Suggests that the author has used some 'writerly' techniques to create suspense as Tom investigates the grandfather clock.
- Draws from pupils some of the techniques for creating suspense (e.g. asking the reader a question, inferring rather than telling, short sentences).
- Gives pupils a photocopy of page 19 and asks them to highlight/annotate examples of these techniques.

INDEPENDENT READING

- Pupils read and annotate the passage.
- Teacher gives support to each pupil, helping them to identify and articulate, for example:

    You think the repetition of 'Hurry! hurry!' builds suspense? Why is that?

RETURNING TO THE TEXT (DISCUSSION)

The teacher asks the pupils to identify and evaluate the different techniques the author uses to create suspense.

FOLLOW-UP INDEPENDENT WORK/ FURTHER READING

Teacher gives specific tasks to be completed before next guided reading session:
- Read to the end of chapter 6.
- Note down in reading journal a few sentences that Tom might have written in his letters to Peter about what has happened to him and how he feels about it.
- What happens to time when Tom is in the garden?
- Any responses/questions about the story so far.

TOM'S MIDNIGHT GARDEN
WHOLE TEXT: SESSION 2

TEACHING OBJECTIVES

- To use a reading notebook effectively to raise and refine responses to text and prepare for discussion.
- To write from another character's point of view, e.g. retelling an incident in letter form.

INTRODUCTION (INCLUDING RESPONDING TO THE TEXT)

Teacher:
- Outlines teaching objectives.
- Checks all pupils have read to end of chapter 6.
- Asks two or three pupils to read out their sentences that Tom might have written. Prompts group discussion on what is revealed about Tom's feelings from his words and actions.
- Goes on to discuss what happens to time when Tom is in the garden. Explains that time has a central part to play in this novel and that in their independent work and discussion they will be looking at the way Philippa Pearce handles time.
- Draws out any other responses pupils have recorded in their notebooks.

FOLLOW-UP INDEPENDENT TASK/ FURTHER READING

Teacher gives specific tasks to be completed before next session:
- Read to the end of chapter 18.
- Note down in reading notebooks:
  a) details about the second main character in the story – Hatty – who is introduced in chapter 8. They could use a table like the following:

Chapter	What we find out about Hatty in this chapter	Estimated age of Hatty

  b) any personal responses/questions they have about the story as they read.

TOM'S MIDNIGHT GARDEN
WHOLE TEXT: SESSION 3

TEACHING OBJECTIVES

- To understand aspects of narrative structure, e.g. how authors handle time (flashbacks, stories within stories, dreams).
- To use a reading notebook effectively to raise and refine personal responses to the text and prepare for discussion.
- To investigate how characters are presented, referring to the text:
  - through dialogue, action and description;
  - how the reader responds to them (as victims, heroes, etc.);
  - through examining their relationships with other characters.

INTRODUCTION (INCLUDING RESPONDING TO THE TEXT)

Teacher:
- Outlines teaching objectives.
- Checks all pupils have read to the end of chapter 18.
- Asks pupils to share what they have found out about Hatty and noted down in their reading journals.
- Through questioning and their own contribution helps pupils to identify the ways the author has provided this information, for example:

  When Hatty's aunt tells her off (see chapter 12, p. 97) what does this incident tell us about Hatty and her situation?

- Asks pupils to give evidence drawn from dialogue and action to justify their growing picture of the character of Hatty, for example:
  Where does it imply that Hatty is frightened of her aunt?
- Asks what they have noted about Hatty's age in these chapters. [They should have noticed that it changes (particularly in chapter 12, p.100: 'a younger Hatty'.]
- Explains that as they read the rest of the book independently they are going to be considering carefully the evidence for Hatty's age.
- Discusses any other responses pupils have recorded in their notebooks.

FOLLOW-UP INDEPENDENT TASK

Teacher gives specific tasks to be completed before the next session:
- Read to the end of the book.
- Note down in their reading journals:
  a) details about Hatty's changing age. Pupils could use a table like this:

Chapter	Evidence that Hatty has changed age	Estimated age of Hatty based on this evidence

b) any personal responses/questions they have now that they have finished *Tom's Midnight Garden*.

TOM'S MIDNIGHT GARDEN
WHOLE TEXT: SESSION 4

TEACHING OBJECTIVES

- To use a reading journal effectively to raise and refine responses to text and to prepare for discussion.
- To write a brief synopsis of a text, e.g. for a back cover blurb.
- To understand how authors handle time.

INTRODUCTION (INCLUDING RESPONDING TO THE TEXT)

Teacher:
- Outlines teaching objectives.
- Checks all pupils have read to the end of the book.
- Asks for and discusses pupils' response to the end of the book:

> What do we know about Hatty now? How do we know that?
> Did you find the ending satisfying? Why? Why not?

offer your own thoughts and feelings, for example:

> I thought the ending was very effective, particularly the last sentence which reminds us that all adults are grown up children, but also pulls together all the narrative threads of the story. Would you agree, Tommy?

- Asks pupils to share their tracking of Hatty's increasing age as the story progressed and the evidence for the observations.
- Discusses the author's manipulation of time:

> How did Tom manage to slip back in time, each night? Is he dreaming, or does it really happen?

> So you think Mrs Bartholomew has something to do with Tom's time travel? In what way?

- Finishes by discussing any of pupils' personal responses they offer now they have finished the story.

FOLLOW-UP INDEPENDENT WORK/ FURTHER READING

- Pupils could write a synopsis/blurb for a new edition of *Tom's Midnight Garden*, for display, as an encouragement for others to read the story.

<table>
<tr><td>

GUIDED READING

YEAR 6

LONGER NOVEL EXTRACT

</td><td>

TOM'S MIDNIGHT GARDEN (p. 19)
Philippa Pearce

Puffin (2000)

ISBN 0141300663

This exemplar demonstrates how an extract from a shared text can be used for a guided reading session.

</td></tr>
</table>

TEACHING OBJECTIVES	<ul><li>To analyse the success of writers in evoking particular responses in the reader, e.g. where suspense is well built.</li><li>To annotate passages in detail in response to specific questions.</li></ul>
TEXT SELECTION NOTES	The specific passage from the book (p .19) has been selected because it shows the author using a range of techniques for building suspense. These include:<ul><li>asking the reader questions</li><li>inferring rather than telling</li><li>short sentences</li><li>repetition.</li></ul>
LINKS TO WHOLE-CLASS TEACHING	*Tom's Midnight Garden* is being used as the basis of a sequence of Literacy Hours over a three-week period. It is a classic work of fiction and many text- and sentence-level objectives both for reading and writing are being taught through the use of this text. These objectives include:<ul><li>Taking account of the viewpoint and identifying the narrator.</li><li>Contributing constructively to shared discussion about literature, responding to and building on the views of others.</li><li>Revising the use and construction of complex sentences.</li><li>Investigating connecting words and phrases.</li><li>Looking at how authors handle time through flashbacks and time shifts.</li></ul>
BEFORE THE SESSION	<ul><li>Teacher ensures that each pupil has a photocopy of page 19 and that there are enough highlighter pens for individuals/pairs.</li><li>Pupils as a class have at least read to the end of chapter 3.</li></ul>
TEXT INTRODUCTION AND DISCUSSION	Teacher:<ul><li>Asks pupils to briefly summarise events up to the beginning of chapter 3.</li><li>Draws attention to the fact that the author has used some techniques to create suspense as Tom investigates the grandfather clock.</li></ul>

- Asks pupils to outline some of the techniques for creating suspense (e.g. asking the reader a question, inferring rather than telling, short sentences).
- Gives pupils the photocopy of page 19 and asks them to highlight/annotate examples of these techniques.

INDEPENDENT READING

- Pupils read and annotate the passage.
- Teacher gives support to each pupil, helping them to identify and articulate, for example:

  You think the repetition of 'Hurry! Hurry!' builds suspense? Why is that?

RETURNING TO THE TEXT

Teacher asks the pupils to identify and evaluate the different techniques the author uses to create suspense, for example:

Does this passage succeed in creating suspense? Why?

LINK TO INDEPENDENT WORK/ FURTHER READING

Pupils read to the end of chapter 3 and note one or two further examples in their reading notebooks.

GUIDED READING

YEAR 6

LONGER NOVEL FILM ADAPTATION

TOM'S MIDNIGHT GARDEN

Directed by Willard Carroll

1998

TEACHING OBJECTIVES

- To compare and evaluate a novel and its film version.
- To examine the treatment of plot and characters.
- To compare the differences in establishing the setting.
- To compare the difference in 'telling' the story with and without a narrator.
- To explore the ways in which time-slip are conveyed in film and text.

TEXT SELECTION NOTES

The Willard Carroll film adds a **frame** around the story of *Tom's Midnight Garden*. It opens with the adult Tom revisiting the old house. The ending shows that the tree on which he and Hatty once carved their initials is in his garden. Thus the story re-inhabits the rural setting and emphasises nostalgia in the deliberate appeal to a family rather than exclusively child audience. The film version also suggests that Aunt Gwen and Uncle Andrew are using Tom's visit to help them decide whether they would like to have children of their own – an adult rather than child's perspective.

LINKS WITH WHOLE-CLASS TEACHING

The teacher has been reading *Tom's Midnight Garden* as the class novel.
- In **shared reading** the class have explored the complex themes and narrative structure.
- **Before viewing** the Willard Carroll film, the class brainstormed initial ideas about the different ways in which stories are told in films and books.
- They have reread the description of the old house and drawn a picture with captions from the text to show how they imagine it will be depicted in the film.
- The class watched the Willard Carroll film.
- **After viewing**, the initial brainstorm was reviewed and further points added. The scenes they had drawn were compared with the film and any differences were noted.
- In shared reading the class have viewed for a second time the scene where Tom first enters the garden. They have identified techniques used to show that Tom has travelled back in time.

BEFORE THE GUIDED READING SESSION

- Pupils were asked to reread chapter 3 'By moonlight' in the book of *Tom's Midnight Garden*.
- Teacher has devised a grid for comparing film and book versions of the text.

GUIDED READING SESSION

INTRODUCTION AND RESPONDING TO THE TEXT(S)

- Teacher asks what clues are there in chapter 3 which indicate that Tom has travelled back in time.
- Pupils are then asked to complete a list of clues that the film version uses for the same purpose.

Book	Film

- Pupils in pairs compile lists.
- Teacher intervenes as pupils discuss and supports discussion.

RETURNING TO THE TEXT

- Pupils share clues and discuss why the differences between book and film occur.
- Teacher chairs and prompts discussion focusing on why the differences occur in the two different types of text.

GUIDED READING	**MILO'S WOLVES** **Jenny Nimmo**
YEAR 6	Mammoth (2001)
	ISBN 0749736755
COMPARISON OF WORKS BY THE SAME AUTHOR	
More challenging	

TEACHING OBJECTIVES

- To describe and evaluate the style of an individual writer.
- To look at the way setting is depicted in *Milo's Wolves* and evaluate the importance of place to the story and the effect this has on the reader.

TEXT SELECTION NOTES

Jenny Nimmo has achieved a reputation as an excellent writer of fantasy fiction. She was awarded the Smarties Grand Prix and Tir na n-Og Award for *The Snow Spider*. *Griffin's Castle* was shortlisted for the Smarties, Whitbread and Carnegie awards.

Laura's parents, Mary and Milo, were involved in a cloning experiment and years later their family must face the consequences of this. This modern 'Frankenstein' story is accessible in style but its themes are complex; *Milo's Wolves* may appeal to readers who respond to conceptual challenge but are less receptive to linguistic challenges.

LINK TO WHOLE-CLASS WORK

The author study is a four-week unit. From a list of possible authors drawn up by the teacher the pupils have elected to study Jenny Nimmo. The current class novel is *The Snow Spider*, which the teacher started to read earlier so that the pupils would have a shared experience before engaging in the author study.

Each guided group is reading a different novel allocated on the basis of the complexity of themes and language. The groups have been reading their novels during independent reading and at home. Each week, time is allocated to sharing what has been read in 'jigsaw' groups. Each group of six children forms a 'home group' to read and discuss one of Jenny Nimmo's books. Each child takes one aspect to prepare a short report on, e.g. setting, character, plot, themes. The children reform into expert groups comprising all those with the same task. All of the children investigating character, for instance, will look at similarities and differences in characterisation in the range of Jenny Nimmo's books. After discussing in expert groups the children reform in their home groups and report back what they have found out. Finally they might prepare a display on the book they have been reading or a report to the class. This activity allows all children to contribute fully to the outcome of the author study.

In the first guided session the group discussed features of *Milo's Wolves* that they felt had some connection with *The Snow Spider*. This is the second guided session.

TEXT INTRODUCTION

Teacher:
- Using the flipchart notes from the previous session, reminds the group of the main points from their discussion.
- Explains that today's guided session is going to focus on one element: the ways in which Jenny Nimmo creates a sense of place in her writing. Two contrasting passages describing the same scene are going to be read and studied.

RESPONDING TO THE TEXT

Teacher:
- Tells pupils to open the book at page 150.
- Asks one pupil to read aloud from 'And then I was moving …' to 'The awful loneliness it conveyed made me shiver.'
- Leads discussion about sense of place by asking: How does the way the castle is described make you feel? Does the scene remind you of any other stories you have read? How does Jenny Nimmo describe the castle?

- Draws out some of the following from pupils:
  Large scale and great age: vast stone-flagged hall, arched at the top and very ancient looking
  Emptiness: table empty, chairs unoccupied, the awful loneliness it conveyed made me shiver, tall desolate castle
  Objects suggest wealth: long, polished table set for dinner, tall silver candlesticks, gold painted bowls of fruit, sparkling glass goblets
  Verbs match the grandeur of the place: 'I *approached* another door'; 'I felt steps *descending* beneath me'; '*Treading* the smooth floor of a narrow passage'.

INDEPENDENT READING

- In pairs the pupils read the passage on page 166 and make notes as for the first passage. From 'We followed him …' to 'I dropped my rucksack and made for the fire.'
- Teacher monitors pairs and checks that pupils are identifying elements which establish sense of place.

RESPONSE TO THE TEXT

Teacher:
- Guides the group to identify contrasts in the way the scene is described:
  Light: lamps cast a rich golden glow, round skylight that showed us the moon
  Warmth: flagstone floor was scattered with Persian carpets, sofas plump and leathery, leaping flames in the great stone fireplace.
- Prompts pupils to consider why Jenny Nimmo has described the same scene in contrasting ways: Does the second description help the reader predict what might happen in the story?
- Leads final reflection: Are the settings in *Milo's Wolves* important for the story? Could the story take place anywhere?

LINK TO INDEPENDENT WORK/ FURTHER READING

The teacher asks the children to continue reading to the end of *Milo's Wolves*. In preparation for the final guided session they are asked to record their views about the actions of Mary, Milo and Jean throughout the story.

GUIDED READING

YEAR 6

DIFFERENT POETS' TREATMENT OF THE SAME THEME

More challenging

OWL
David Harsent
In *Swings and Shadows: Poems of Childhood*
Edited by A. Harvey

Red Fox (2001)

ISBN 0099646811

AN AUGUST MIDNIGHT
Thomas Hardy
In *Poems of the Past and the Present*

Macmillan (1901)

TEACHING OBJECTIVE	To identify ways in which linked poems relate to each other in terms of theme, format and style.
LINK TO WHOLE-CLASS WORK	After a period of browsing, the children have selected poetry anthologies that have appealed to them. They have presented reasons for their choices in small groups. The teacher has prompted them to think about the qualities of a good anthology. Some of the issues they have considered include:

- a range of favourite poems as well as less well-known poems
- inclusion of classic and contemporary poetry
- good opening poems, good closing poems
- juxtaposing one poem against another
- range of moods
- role of illustrations
- inclusion of anthologists' notes explaining their choices.

The class is producing an anthology of their own writing. The class teacher has been encouraging the children to reflect on the process of writing. Do they enjoy it? Is it hard? Challenging? Rewarding? What obstacles do they find difficult to overcome? To tie in with this work, the teacher has selected poems that share the theme of reflecting on the process of writing poetry.

BEFORE THE GUIDED READING SESSION	• Both poems have been read aloud by more than one reader prior to the guided reading session. • Pupils in the group have been given both poems to read before the session and asked to think about any similarities between them.

INTRODUCTION (INCLUDING RETURNING TO THE TEXT)

- Pupils outline whether they saw any similarities. Teacher encourages other pupils to add or contradict (in a constructive fashion!).
- Supplementary questions by teacher might guide the groups to consider such questions as:

  Who is telling us this story? Where? What time of day?
  Explain how you know.

  (NB Do not over-use these questions to avoid this becoming a question-and-answer session.)

INDEPENDENT READING

One member of the group acts as scribe and the group agrees on a list of similarities and differences, for example:

SIMILARITIES	DIFFERENCES
Subject • Speaker is the poet • Late at night • Both poets are writing • Reflect on the activity of night creatures	Form • Effect of rhyme
	Significance of the creatures • Hardy's sleepy minibeasts • Harsent's predatory owl
	Tone of last lines • Hardy's wonder: 'God's humblest they!' I muse. 'Yet why?/They know Earth-secrets that know not I.'
Theme • Reflection on the process of writing	• Harsent: Caring nothing at all for words And nothing at all for the writers of words.

RESPONDING TO THE TEXT

- Pupils explain to the teacher their decisions.
- Teacher prompts to clarify the theme of both poets' reflections on the process of writing.
- Session concludes by pupils being asked to consider:

  Has anything surprised you about the writers' thoughts or feelings?
  Why was it surprising?

LINK TO INDEPENDENT WORK/ FURTHER READING

- Pupils could investigate and share examples of things other writers have said about writing from the teacher's resource bank. For example:

Agard, J. (1996) 'Poetry jump up', in *Get Back Pimple!* London: Viking 0670861987.

Hughes, T. (1995) 'The thought fox', in *Collected Animal Poems 4: The Thought Fox*. London: Faber and Faber 0571176283.

AN AUGUST MIDNIGHT

A shaded lamp and a waving blind,
And the beat of a clock from a distant floor:
On this scene enter – winged horned, horned and spined –
A longlegs, a moth and a dumbledore;
While 'mid my page there idly stands
A sleepy fly that rubs its hands.....

Thus meet we five, in this still place,
At this point of time, at this point in space.
My guests besmear my new penned line.
Or bang at the lamp and fall supine.
'God's humblest they!' I muse. 'Yet why?
They know Earth-secrets that know not I.'

Thomas Hardy

OWL

As I was sitting, late last night,
At my desk by the window, trying to write,

Trying to find the phrase, the word,
To make the poem come right, I heard

The screech of an owl, and saw him streak
Down to strike with claw and beak,

Then turn, with churning wings to rise
Into the echoes of his cries.

When he was out of sight, I sank
Back in my chair, pushing the blank

Sheets of paper aside and then
Turned out the lamp, put down my pen,

And sat in the dark to think of the owl,
Who is guileless, neither kind nor cruel,

Who lives without the need for thought
And hunts with skills that can't be taught,

Who kills without hatred, without guilt
Strips the flesh from the furry pelt,

Caring nothing at all for words
And nothing at all for the writers of words.

David Harsent

GUIDED READING

YEAR 6

DIFFERENT AUTHORS' TREATMENT OF THE SAME THEME

THE TUNNEL
Anthony Browne

Walker Books (1989)

ISBN 0744552397

BEWARE BEWARE
Susan Hill and Angela Barrett

Walker Books (1993)

ISBN 0744536626

TEACHING OBJECTIVES

- To look at connections and contrasts in the work of different authors.
- To revise the language conventions and grammatical features of narrative texts.

The objectives of the sessions are principally concerned with refining children's responses and developing comprehension to allow for differentiated work through questioning and discussion. In this case the children will benefit from sharing their interpretations with others. The guided sessions set up a challenging reading experience during which the teacher explicitly supports pupils in the application of comprehension strategies.

TEXT SELECTION NOTES

Both texts are picture books in which the narrative is conveyed through the interplay of words and pictures. They offer multi-layered, challenging reading experiences which can be explored within a guided reading session.

The Tunnel is both written and illustrated by Anthony Browne, a highly acclaimed picture book maker who won the prestigious Hans Andersen Award for outstanding achievement in 2000. His other picture books include *Hansel and Gretel*, *Changes*, *Gorilla*, *Zoo*.

Beware Beware is the outcome of a collaborative endeavour between the author Susan Hill and illustrator Angela Barrett. Susan Hill writes for adults and children; her work for children includes *Can it be True?* Angela Barrett's use of soft pastels for imaginative depth can also be seen in her interpretation of Martin Waddell's *The Hidden House*.

The two books will have some striking similarities. For example:
- Home–away–home structure
- Reference to fairy stories in the language and visual motifs
- Windows, used to show a view of the unknown but also to represent imaginative freedom
- Contrast of interior and exterior settings
- Forest as landscape of the mind
- Developing independence
- Overcoming fear.

The books also contrast in significant ways. The teacher has drawn up a list of contrasts:

Here are some of the contrasts that I observed. After reading the books you will be able to draw up your own lists.

The Tunnel	Beware Beware
Contemporary/urban	19th century rural
Sister/brother relationship	Mother/daughter relationship
Third-person narrative	Poetic monologue
Mother sends children away from home The girl does not want to leave	Girl is curious about the forest and visits without mother's knowledge
Some sense of closure	Tenuous closure

LINKS TO WHOLE-CLASS WORK

In shared reading sessions the class have been reading *The Tunnel*. They have discussed the connections with Red Riding Hood and Hansel and Gretel and have been encouraged to bring in other versions of these folktales for independent reading. In shared reading they have also looked at the narrative structure and have constructed a story map. They have looked at language that is characteristic of the traditional folktale: 'one morning their mother grew impatient …'; '… and so she waited …'; 'she found herself in a quiet wood'.

They have talked about the theme of the book as an underlying idea and have listed themes in *The Tunnel* and other favourite books.

BEFORE THE GUIDED READING SESSION (INDEPENDENT WORK)

In preparation for this guided reading session the group have been asked to take the book *Beware Beware* home to read and to record their initial responses in their reading notebooks. By this stage the children use the notebooks independently to record thoughts, feelings or questions they have about the group text.

BEWARE BEWARE
SESSION 1: RESPONDING AND UNDERSTANDING

INTRODUCTION (INCLUDING RESPONDING TO THE TEXT)

- Each member of the group has a copy of the text.
- Children share their initial responses; these are accepted without comment by the teacher to encourage all members of this mixed-ability group to participate, knowing that their ideas will not be judged.
- Teacher makes notes of responses taking account of the ways in which individual children have chosen to express their responses, interpretation, appreciation, personal significance. She asks them to consider how each other's contributions have extended their own ideas and made them think differently about the book.
- Teacher prompts them to consider why the book is called *Beware Beware*. Are there real dangers in the wood? Is it the little girl's imagination?
- Can the pupils justify their answers with reference to the pictures or the text?
- Teacher asks whether they think it is like any other books they have read. She extends their answers by asking for specific examples/episodes/characters/themes as evidence for their contributions.

INDEPENDENT ACTIVITY

- Pupils are asked to work in pairs to think about the similarities and differences between *Beware Beware* and *The Tunnel*. Each pair is given a copy of each book and makes notes in two headed columns in their reading notebooks. They use a grid such as this one:

	Beware Beware	**The Tunnel**
Setting		
Plot Structure		
Problem(s)		
Solving of Problem		
Theme		
Characters		
Other		

- Teacher explains that this activity will form the basis for the discussion in the next guided reading session.

BEWARE BEWARE
SESSION 2: COMPARING THE TEXTS

INTRODUCTION

- Each member of the group has copies of both texts.
- So far the group have explored their responses and understandings of individual books. In this session they will be comparing and contrasting the two books, thus refining their understanding of each book.

INTRODUCTION (INCLUDING RETURNING TO THE TEXT)

The group talks about the similarities and differences they have noticed in the two books. They compare each book section by section and the teacher prompts them to think about salient points. (See Text Selection Notes.)

RESPONDING TO THE TEXT

In conclusion the pupils are prompted to describe and reflect upon whether their initial response to either book has changed in the light of comparing the two, for example:

John you thought … at the beginning of the last session. Do you still think that? Why? (Why not?)

Amy, what do you think you have learnt about picture books as a result of our two guided reading sessions. Do others think the same?

GUIDED READING

YEAR 6

NON-FICTION

Texts linked to geography topic work

This guided reading exemplar is designed as a quick revision of the main structural features of information texts, practising using these features when retrieving information, and deploying the strategies of skimming and scanning. The first session can then be extended into a second, which compares critically the information found in texts that purport to be about the same area of knowledge.

TEXT SELECTION NOTES

Any selection of texts used for study of distant location – less economically developed – could be used. We have, however listed some texts which typically would form the basis for the second session (p. 132).

TEACHING OBJECTIVES

- To revise main features of non-fiction information text.
- To develop skills of retrieving information from text.
- To compare different non-fiction texts on the same topic.
- To develop critical appreciation skills.

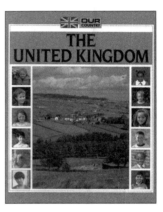

GEOGRAPHY TOPIC WORK
SESSION 1

TEXT INTRODUCTION

- Teacher elicits from pupils the main features of non-fiction text and lists these on flipchart (factual, non-narrative, organised in chapters or sections, contents, index, glossary).
  Pupils check that the books they have contain these features.
- Teacher outlines the teaching objectives, for example:

  In this session we're going to revise how to find the information we want in a book. Let's think about what we might want to find out.

  First – have a look through the book quickly and think of specific questions that you'd like to ask. For example:
  > How many people live in this country?
  > What kinds of food do they eat?
  > What kinds of animals live there?
  > What's the climate like?
  > What are the schools like?

  Then write down your own question.
  Then see if you can find the information to answer your question – turn to the contents page and see if you can find the relevant section. Look it up. Skim that section and see if you can find the answer. If not, have another try.

STRATEGY CHECK

- Teacher elicits from pupils what is meant by skimming and scanning and how the strategies are used on text, for example:

  In your question the key word is *climate*. How do we use that word to help us locate the information on this page? Well done, you spotted the word in the subheading. This is the section that will answer the question. You used scanning to look over the text very quickly and located the key word and then we read around it to get the information we want.

INDEPENDENT READING

- Pupils devise questions and search for relevant information.
- Teacher observes and prompts where necessary assessing whether pupils are using the strategy of scanning in particular.

RETURNING TO THE TEXT

Teacher:
- Works with the group to reinforce any specific teaching points.
- Asks if anyone has **not** found the answer to their question.
- Discusses reasons for this:
  > the question was too specific, for example What kind of information do the books contain? (only general facts)
  > the book being consulted did not have the answer, but other books do Why do authors have to leave some facts out? What kind of facts do they include?
  > the answer might have been found in the illustrations rather than the text itself.

GEOGRAPHY TOPIC WORK
SESSION 2

TEACHING OBJECTIVES

- To compare different non-fiction texts on the same topic.
- To develop critical appreciation skills.

TEXTS

One topic covered in at least three different textbooks, for example farming, education (schools), cities, land and climate (the weather, mountain valleys and passes, plains and rivers) in

Focus on Pakistan, Mano Rumalshah, Evans Brothers 1989.
Pakistan, David Cumming, Wayland 1991 (Our Country series)
Pakistan, David Cumming, Wayland 1989 (Countries of the World series)

TEXT INTRODUCTION

Teacher:
- Outlines teaching objectives.
- Asks pupils to look at each book in turn and note down what information it contains about education in Pakistan. (They could do this in columns.)
- Draws from pupils the strategies they will use to locate this information.
- Tells pupils to look for any differences in the information offered.

INDEPENDENT READING

- Pupils in pairs consider each book in turn.
- Teacher observes, supports information retrieval strategies, and prompts discussion about the information found.

RETURNING TO THE TEXT

Teacher:
- Asks pupils to report back on what they have found.
- Prompts discussion about any differences found.

LINK TO INDEPENDENT WORK/ FURTHER READING

These facts about education, cities, land and climate, etc. could be compared with those in books about the UK. Some publishers have used the same headings to systemise the content, for example the Our Country series published by Wayland (see, for example Christa Stadder, *The United Kingdom*, Wayland 1991).

Pupils could be asked to consider:

Do you feel the information about the UK is correct? Does it give a true picture?
What in the text makes you say that?
Do you think the same might be true about the books about Pakistan?

YEAR 6 BOOK LIST	Author/Editor	Publisher/Date	ISBN
FICTION			
A Christmas Carol	Rosalind Kerven	Literacy World/Heinemann 1998	0435093118 (pack of 6)
A Letter To Daniel	Fergal Keane	Penguin 1996	014026289X
A Midsummer Night's Dream	abridged by Leon Garfield	Heinemann Young Books 1992	0434962333
Beware Beware	Susan Hill	Walker 1993	0744536626
Blitz	Robert Westall	Collins 1995	0006750869
Carrie's War	Nina Bawden	Puffin 1993	0140364560
Chasing Redbird	Sharon Creech	Macmillan 1997	0330342134
Daughter of the Sea	Berlie Doherty	Puffin 1998	0140379517
Double Danger	Mandy Hager	Redcliffe Publishing 2000	0478249233
Eye in the Sky	Janice Marriott	Redcliffe Publishing 2000	0478249268
Forbidden Memories	Jamila Gavin	Mammoth 1998	0749730749
Grandfather Singh Stories	Pratima Mitchell, Wendy Body (ed.)	Longman Book Project (Longman) 1995	058212218X
Hacker	Malorie Blackman	Corgi 1993	0552527513
Heroes and Villains	Tony Bradman	Cambridge Reading Scheme 1998	0521575516
King of Shadows	Susan Cooper	Puffin 2000	0141307994
Krindlekrax	Philip Ridley	Red Fox 1992	0099979209
Lady Daisy	Dick King-Smith	Puffin 1993	0140344160
Letters to Henrietta	Nell Marshall	Cambridge Reading Scheme 1998	0521476259
Marriage of the Rain Goddess	M. O. Wolfson, C. A. Parms (illus.)	Barefoot Books 1998	1901223132
Mercedes Ice	Philip Ridley	Puffin 1996	0140368922
Milo's Wolves	Jenny Nimmo	Mammoth 2001	0749736755
My Dad's Got An Alligator	Jeremy Strong	Puffin 1996	0140365842
Myths, Legends and Monsters	Mick Gowar, Wendy Body (ed.)	Longman Book Project (Longman) 1995	0582122465
Natasha's Will	Joan Lingard	Puffin 2000	0141308923
Over Sea, Under Stone	Susan Cooper	Puffin 1994	0140303626
Planet Boring	Nathan Cook	Redcliffe Publishing 2000	0478249349
Sci-fi Danger!	David Orme (ed.)	Longman 2000	0582433320
Scribble Boy	Philip Ridley	Faber 2002	0571205984
Seth And The Strangers	Jenny Nimmo	Mammoth 1997	0749728841
Sophie And The Seawolf	Helen Cresswell	Hodder Children's Books 1997	0340689862
Star Thief	Morman Bilbrough	Redcliffe Publishing 2000	0478249373
Telling Tales	Barbara Ireson (ed.)	Red Fox 1996	0099543915
The Dolphin's Daughter	Alma Hromic, Wendy Body (ed.)	Longman Book Project 1995	0582122104
The Fib and Other Stories	George Layton	Macmillan Children's 1997	033035227X
The Fireworkmaker's Daughter	Philip Pullman	Yearling 1996	0440863317
The Haunting	Margaret Mahy	Puffin 1992	0140363254
The Hermit Shell	Frances Usher	Cambridge 1998	052155666X
'The Hitchhikers' in The Wonderful Story Of Henry Sugar	Roald Dahl	Puffin 2001	0141311495
The Mouse and his Child	Russell Hoban	Faber & Faber 2000	0571202225
The Paper Bag Prince	Colin Thompson	Red Fox 1994	0099933209
The Refugees	Janice Marriott	Redcliffe Publishing 2000	0478249357
The Rope and Other Stories	Philippa Pearce	Puffin 2000	0141309148
The Sailing Ship Tree	Berlie Doherty	Puffin 2000	0140379525
The Secret Garden	France Hodgson Burnett	Puffin 1994	0140366660
The Tunnel	Anthony Browne	Walker 1997	0744552397
The Turbulent Term of Tyke Tiler	Gene Kemp	Puffin 1979	0140311351
The Wreck Of The Zanzibar	Michael Morpurgo	Mammoth 1995	0749726202
Tom's Midnight Garden	Philippa Pearce	Puffin 2000	0141300663
Trucker	Fleur Beale	Redcliffe Publishing 2000	0478249403
Truth Or Dare	Tony Bradman (ed.)	Cambridge 1998	0521575524
Village by the Sea	Anita Desai	Puffin 2001	0141312718
POETRY			
Collected Animal Poems Vol. 1: The Iron Wolf	Ted Hughes	Faber 1995	0571176224
Lost Property Box	P. Dixon, W. Mager and M. Simpson	Macmillan 1998	0330369679

YEAR 6 BOOK LIST	Author/Editor	Publisher/Date	ISBN
Poetry Jump Up	Grace Nichols	Puffin 1990	014034053X
Rap with Rosen	Michael Rosen *et al.*, Wendy Body (ed.)	Longman Book Project (Longman) 1995	0582122066
Shades of Green	Anne Harvey (ed.)	Faber 1995	0099255219
Talking Turkeys	Benjamin Zephaniah	Puffin 1995	0140363300
Through a Window	Wendy Body (ed.)	Longman Book Project (Longman) 1995	0582122406
You Wait Till I'm Older Than You	Michael Rosen	Puffin 1997	0140380140
NON-FICTION			
A Time in my Life	Wendy Body (ed.)	Pelican (Longman) 2000	0582433207
Amazing Environments	Terry Jennings	Oxford Reading Tree (Oxford) 1995	0199167133
Amazing Journeys	Ron Bacon	Shortland	0790116006
Benjamin Zephaniah	Verna Wilkins	Tamarind 1999	1870516389
Big Issues	Brian Moss	Literacy World (Heinemann) 1999	0435096885
Caring for our Environment	Maureen Crandles, Ann Kite	Oxford Reading Tree (Oxford) 1995	0199167095
Computer	Catherine Chambers	Heinemann 1998	0431086877
Days Of The Knights	Christopher Maynard	Dorling Kindersley 1998	0751357162
Endurance	Janice Marriott	Redcliffe Publishing 2000	047824925X
The First Lunar Landing	Rodney Martin	Rigby 1989	0947212477 (Pack)
The Human Body	Penny Coltman, R. S. Linfield	Longman 1999	0582338921
It'll Be All Right on the Night	Pat Quinn	Redcliffe Publishing 2000	0478249292
Martial Arts	Donna Malane	Redcliffe Publishing 2000	0478249322
Medicine News	Phil Gates	Walker 1997	0744528895
Memories	Mem Fox	Magic Bean 1992	1863740252
Out of India	Jamila Gavin	Hodder Children's Books 1997	0340854626
Playground Detectives	Terry Jennings	Oxford Reading Tree (Oxford) 1995	0199167087
Pollution	Terry Jennings	Oxford Reading Tree (Oxford) 1995	0199167125
Protecting our Wildlife	Terry Jennings	Oxford Reading Tree (Oxford) 1995	0199167109
Quakes, Floods and other Disasters	Fred Martin	Literacy World /Heinemann 2000	0435119931
Rainforest	Barbara Taylor	Dorling Kindersley 1998	0751357669
Road Code: A Highway Code Written for Young Road Users	DETR	Her Majesty's Stationery Office 1999	0115521771
RSPCA	Frazer Swift	Heinemann 1997	0431027560
Secrets of the Mummies	Harriet Griffey	Dorling Kindersley 1998	0751357154
Spiders and How they Hunt		Literacy World /Heinemann 2000	0435096869 (Pack of 6)
Stop Wasting the World	Terry Jennings	Oxford Reading Tree (Oxford) 1995	0199167117
The Highway Code		The Stationery Office	0115519777
Three Tudor Lives	James Mason	Longman 1998	0582299411 (Pack of 6)
Titanic	Mark Dubowski	Dorling Kindersley 1998	0751358606
Twisting up a Storm	Cheryl Duksta	Redcliffe Publishing 2000	0478249411
Volcanoes	Jenny Wood	Two-Can Publishing 1990	1854340077
Volcanoes and other Natural Disasters	Harriet Griffey	Dorling Kindersley 1998	0751357170
War Boy: A Country Childhood	Michael Foreman	Puffin 1991	0140342990
What in the World is the World Wide Web?	Pat Quinn	Redcliffe Publishing 2000	0478249446
Wreck Trek	Angie Belcher	Redcliffe Publishing 2000	0478249454
Writer's Lives	Dennis Hamley	Longman 1998	0582334144
You Can Make Your Own Book	Paul Johnson	Longman 1999	0582337380
MEDIA			
Alice Through the Looking Glass	Lewis Carroll	Channel 4 Book Box	
Robinson Crusoe		Tivola Software	
The Odyssey		Channel 4 Book Box	
LEAFLETS			
Planting a Pond		B&Q 2001	
MORE CHALLENGING LITERARY TEXTS FOR YEAR 6 PUPILS			
A Little Lower than the Angels	Geraldine McCaughrean	Oxford (new edn) 1998	0192717804
Alice in Wonderland (unabridged)	Lewis Carroll	Puffin 1994	0140620869

YEAR 6 BOOK LIST	Author/Editor	Publisher/Date	ISBN
Apples	Laurie Lee	in *Literacy Time* 5/6 No. 12 – Scholastic 2001	ISSN 14659018
Bridge to Terabithia	Katherine Patterson	Puffin 1995	0140312609
Candlefasts	William Mayne	Hodder (new edn) 2000	0340757531
Collected Animal Poems Vol. 2: What is the Truth?	Ted Hughes	Oxford 1994	0571176240
Cradlefasts	William Mayne	Hodder 1995	0340651261
Earthfasts	William Mayne	Hodder 1995	0340653272
Goodnight Mister Tom	Michelle Magorian	Puffin 1993	0140372334
Heaven Eyes	David Almond	Hodder Wayland 2000	0340743689
Holes	Louis Sachar	Bloomsbury 2000	0747551405
John Bunyan's A Pilgrim's Progress	Geraldine McCaughrean	Hodder Children's Books 2001	0340844108
POW	Martin Booth	Puffin 2000	0141304219
Scottish Poems	John Rice (ed.)	Macmillan 2001	0333900731
Skellig	David Almond	Chivers 1999	0754060667
Smith	Leon Garfield	Puffin 1970	0140303499
The Kite Rider	Geraldine McCaughrean	Oxford 2001	0192718606
The New Young Oxford Book of Ghost Stories	Dennis Pepper (ed.)	Oxford 2000	0192781782
The Other Side of Truth	Beverley Naidoo	Puffin 2000	0141304766
The Oxford Book of Children's Verses	Iona and Peter Opie (eds)	Oxford 1994	0192823493
The Oxford Treasury of Classic Poems	M. Harrison and C. Stuart-Clark (eds)	Oxford 1997	0192761870
The Owl Service	Alan Garner	Collins 1960	0006742947
The Wedding Ghost	Leon Garfield	Oxford 1999	0192723952
Where Were you Robert?	Hans Magnus Enzenberger	Puffin 2001	0141306807
Another resource for guided reading recommended by literacy consultants, which is not linked to year groups:			
Literacy Time 5/6 magazine		published by Scholastic	

PART 5

What teachers need to know about text types

INTRODUCTION

In this section you will find explanations about the range of texts that are suggested in the *NLS Framework for teaching*. Our aim is to enable teachers to extend their knowledge about texts in order to teach with greater confidence and expertise. In the tables that follow we have outlined some of the characteristic features of texts and have expanded the main points in a brief commentary. If your interest is keen and you would like to take this further, a supplementary reading list is included in Part 7. You may want to draw upon this reading to develop your understanding of different text types, as we do not have space in this current publication to cover more than the main generic features. The terminology that we have used is primarily for the teacher's benefit and we do not suggest that it should be directly transported into the classroom, although the prompts do suggest starting points for talking about text features with guided reading groups. The prompt questions are, of course, only a starting point and you will want to adapt them to suit the needs of your groups and the texts you are reading. A full description of the questions that promote good book talk can be found in Aidan Chambers' book *Tell Me* (1993).

Note on abbreviations

We refer to the targets in the *NLS Framework for teaching* in abbreviated form. So, for example, Y3 t2 *T1* means Year 3, term 2, text level 1.

SELECTING TEXTS

There are some general factors that you will want to take into consideration when selecting texts for guided reading groups. The following questions are not intended to be a checklist but are offered as aids to thinking. Identifying the level of challenge is a critical part of the preparation for guided reading and it is important to ensure that reading groups of all abilities are both challenged and supported in their learning. Therefore when choosing a text that is conceptually complex it might be necessary to ensure that the style and language are relatively straightforward and do not inhibit the reader's engagement with the challenging content.

Conceptual complexity and challenge

- Does the text offer an appropriate balance between conceptual challenge and accessibility?
- Does the text present interesting ways of exploring the world and describing human experience?
- Are underlying ideas unusual or complex?
- Is there scope for multiple readings or interpretation?
- Is the subject matter familiar or will it extend the knowledge of the group?
- Is the content likely to be of interest to the group?
- Are there opportunities for integrating the guided reading sessions with other aspects of the curriculum?

Emotional complexity

- Are issues thoughtfully presented?
- Are readers invited to evaluate and make judgements?
- Are decisions presented within the text always easy or are there a number of choices that could be made?
- What value judgements are implied by the text? Can these judgements be explored with the group?
- Do the texts chosen over a period allow children to experience a range of emotions? To laugh, to cry, to be joyful and to shudder?

Organisation and structure	• Are there clear structures of organisation? • Are time sequences or chronology presented in interesting ways? • Are cohesive links made between different parts of the text?
Language and style	• Is language used in interesting and original ways? • Is vocabulary challenging? Are there many technical words that are likely to be new to the reader? • Is the syntax challenging? Are there many sentences of unusual or difficult construction?
Appeal	• Does the text appeal to you and is it likely to appeal to the pupils?

MORE THAN A SUM OF THE PARTS

One of the potential dangers in presenting tables of text features is that reading lessons can become too heavily directed by narrowly focused objectives. The true value of a poem cannot, for example, be elicited through analysis of discrete elements such as rhyme, rhythm and diction. Although we might talk about the way in which a poet has employed a particular rhyme scheme, this should always be done with regard to thinking about how this illuminates our understanding of the impact of the poem.

It is essential that pupils' experiences with literature provide opportunities for expression and refinement of personal responses. The NLS framework identifies objectives that are fundamentally concerned with the development of positive and enquiring attitudes towards reading. A brief survey of these objectives shows that although they have been listed at specific points in the termly curriculum, they are most appropriately addressed on a continuous basis, forming the bedrock of a reading policy:

• read further stories by a favourite author
• express own views about stories
• develop an awareness of authors and express preferences
• develop an active attitude towards reading, seeking answers and anticipating events
• empathise with characters and imagine events that are described
• contribute constructively to a shared discussion about literature, responding to and building on the views of others.

VISUAL TEXTS: PICTURE BOOKS, FILM AND TELEVISION

In Part 4 we have included exemplars which use picture books and film extracts as challenging texts (pp. 126–9, 118–19). Many of the features described in the following tables can be applied to picture book and media texts, for example narrative structure or realisation of character and setting. However, the languages employed by visual texts are unique. For instance in talking about picture books we might look at the way an artist has used colour, line and shape as well as looking at the cultural and artistic traditions that have informed the work. Recommendations for further reading are given in Part 7 (pp. 183–95).

NARRATIVE FICTION: GENERIC FEATURES

Features	NLS Framework	Prompt Questions

PLOT, NARRATIVE STRUCTURE
 	
Events of a story
 	
Order of events
 	
Story shape
	• Retell main point as a story sequence (Y3 t3 *T1*)
	• Explore chronology in narrative by mapping how much time passes, by noticing where there are jumps in time or where some events are skimmed quickly and others are mapped in detail (Y4 t1 *T3*)
	• Explore narrative order: identify and map out the main stages of the story; introductions … build-ups … climaxes … resolutions (Y4 t1 *T4*)
	• Analyse the features of a good opening and compare a number of story openings (Y5 t1 *T1*)
	• Compare the structure of different stories to discover how they differ in pace, build-up, sequence, complication and resolution (Y5 t1 *T2*)
	• Understand aspects of narrative structure, e.g.
	   how chapters in books are linked together
	   how authors handle time: flashbacks, stories within stories, dreams
	   how the passing of time is conveyed to the reader (Y6 t2 *T1*)
		• How long did the story take?
		• Did the events happen in the order we are told about them in the story?
		• Why do you think the writer chose to tell us about events in this order?
		• Are there some parts of the story that happen in a short time but take a long time to describe?
		• Are there some parts of the story that happen over a long period but are told very quickly?

NARRATIVE FICTION: GENERIC FEATURES

Commentary

Plot is often considered to be of particular importance in writing for children, comprising the action and sequence of events.

Narrative structure is determined by the function that is fulfilled by different elements of the story. Commentators have described it in various ways; the following framework is adapted from Longacre (1976).

Story frame: may be placed around the story before the main story begins. In *Carrie's War* by Nina Bawden, for example, the adult Carrie returns to Druids' Bottom with her own children at the beginning and then the story ends with Carrie's reunion with Hepzibah Green and Mister Johnny.

Aperture: the first words of a story opening. Most conventionally, the fairytale 'Once upon a time' or 'Long, long ago in a land east of the sun and west of the moon there lived'.

Exposition: contains vital information about setting (time and place) and character.

Inciting moment: this is the moment when the predictability of the exposition is broken. For example in *Hansel and Gretel* this occurs when the stepmother insists that her husband take the children into the woods to abandon them.

Developing conflict: the action of the story intensifies. Sometimes this element might be called the complication. The part of the story where tensions are built can be called the rising action.

Climax: the part of the story where matters come to a head. Climaxes vary in intensity and how close they come to the end of the story. In J.K. Rowling's *Harry Potter and the Goblet of Fire*, the climax (Harry's face-to-face battle with the evil Voldemort) occurs two chapters before the end of the book.

Denouement: a crucial final event occurs which makes a resolution possible. In Philippa Pearce's *Tom's Midnight*

Garden, Tom finally meets Mrs Bartholomew and discovers that she is Hatty from the garden. From the denouement the story enters a phase of falling action.

Final suspense: the details of the resolution are worked out. Tom works out that it is old Mrs Bartholomew's dreaming that connects him with the garden.

Conclusion: a satisfactory ending is worked out. For the characters this does not necessarily mean that they live happily ever after. Conclusions can be left open-ended, though this is not common in children's fiction. Closed endings tie up the loose ends. Younger readers may prefer stories with closure where the emphasis is on the restoration of normality but stories with a strong closure may have problems with credibility. The comforting ending of E. Nesbit's *The Railway Children* is criticised by some readers as lapsing into unbelievable wish fulfilment.

Sometimes the conclusion includes a coda: a reiteration of the story's moral.

Story shapes

Plots may follow the standard narrative presentation outlined above. However, not all elements are present in every story and in longer, more complex narratives there may be a spiral of developing conflict with a series of mini climaxes.

A linear plot adheres to a strict chronological order and does not rise to a climax. One such example is Sharon Creech's *Walk Two Moons*.

The bildungsroman is concerned with the main character's personal development. Tolkien's *The Hobbit* is essentially about Bilbo Baggins's coming of age.

Another structure often found in children's books is the episodic story. Each chapter is a self-contained adventure. For example, in E. Nesbit's *Five Children and It* each chapter describes what happens when the Psammead grants the children a wish.

NARRATIVE FICTION: GENERIC FEATURES

Features	NLS Framework	Prompt Questions
SETTING **Describes time and place**	• Compare a range of story settings, selecting words and phrases to describe scenes (Y3 t1 *T1*) • Understand how writers create imaginary worlds (Y4 t2 *T1*) • Understand how settings influence events and incidents in stories and how they affect characters' behaviour (Y4 t2 *T2*) • Compare and contrast settings across a range of stories; to evaluate, form preferences (Y4 t2 *T3*) • Compare and evaluate a novel and film version looking at the different ways in which setting is realised in the two forms (Y6 t1 *T1*)	• Where did this story take place? • Is the setting really important to the story or could it have happened anywhere? • Was the setting for this story familiar or unfamiliar to you? • Did you get a really clear picture of where this story was set? • Do any particular words or phrases help you to imagine the place where this story was set? • Do any words or phrases provide an indication of the time when this story is taking place?

NARRATIVE FICTION: GENERIC FEATURES

Commentary

The setting of a story describes the time and place in which the actions occur. In some stories the setting is incidental, simply providing a backdrop for the action. *Rosie's Babies* by Penny Dale tells a story in which imaginative play and a supportive mother are important elements in helping Rosie come to terms with the arrival of a new baby. The illustrations depict an idyllic pastoral setting in which Rosie plays with her soft toys in a beautiful orchard. But the plot and theme could have been successfully explored if the story had been set in an urban tower block, or suburban terrace. For other stories, however, the setting is integral to the tale. Alan Garner's fantasy *The Owl Service* and Jenny Nimmo's *Snow Spider* trilogy are set in Wales, where every tree and stone is steeped in the mythology of *The Mabinogion*. In Garner's story in particular the setting itself becomes the main antagonist, which must be confronted by the three children who are drawn into a conflict that emanates from the ancient history of the place.

An author's description of setting can develop a reader's belief in the story, perhaps through realistic depiction of a place or period; in historical fiction, for instance, the setting can add authentic detail. High fantasy is dependent on the believable creation of a secondary world and science fiction similarly requires successfully realised futuristic settings.

But setting is not always used to evoke a sense of realism, it can also operate at a symbolic level. In traditional stories such as *Hansel and Gretel* the forest can be interpreted as the manifestation of anxiety and may also represent personal growth from dependence to independence. Anthony Browne's picture book of this Grimm's tale emphasises the psychological symbolism.

Film and television adaptations of books realise setting differently from written text, which rarely describes setting in the minute detail that locations and prop teams have to in order to create visual scenes. Also, in film adaptations of novels locations may be changed; for example settings in the film versions of Mary Norton's *The Borrowers*, Anne Fine's *Madame Doubtfire* and Lynn Reid Banks's *The Indian in the Cupboard* were all changed from Britain to America. Young readers can discuss the impact this has on the stories and should be encouraged to consider why such decisions are made.

NARRATIVE FICTION: GENERIC FEATURES

Features	NLS Framework	Prompt Questions

POINT OF VIEW
 	
Who is telling the story?
 	
From whose point of view do we learn about characters and events?
	• Be aware of different voices; between the narrator and different characters (Y3 t1 *T3*)
	• Distinguish between first- and third-person accounts (Y3 t3 *T3*)
	• Distinguish between the author and narrator, investigating narrative treatment of different characters (Y5 t2 *T8*)
	• Identify the point of view from which a story is told and how this affects response (Y5 t3 *T2*)
	• Change point of view, e.g. tell incident or describe a situation from the point of view of another character or perspective (Y5 t3 *T3*)
	• Take account of the viewpoint in a novel through, e.g.
	    identifying the narrator
	    explaining how this influences the reader's view of events
	    explaining how events might look from a different point of view (Y6 t1 *T2*)
		• Who is telling this story?
		• How do you know who is telling the story?
		• Is the story told in the first or third person?
		• Who do you feel closest to in this story? Can you say why?
		• Through whose eyes do you think you are seeing this story?
		• When you were reading did you feel you were part of this story or did you feel you were an observer?

NARRATIVE FICTION: GENERIC FEATURES

Commentary

Point of view is concerned with the narration: who is telling the story and from whose point of view do we learn about characters and events? Narration may be personal, often referred to as first-person narration. Most frequently the first person narrator is one of the characters in the story. E. Nesbit was one of the earliest writers for children to experiment with first-person narration. She attempted to give the impression that the children were telling their own stories and tried to avoid an overbearing tone of wise adult narrator to naïve child narratee. Personal narration may imply an autobiographical voice such as in Michael Morpurgo's *Wreck of the Zanzibar*, which opens with the narrator describing a return to the Scilly Isles for the funeral of his great aunt Laura and the discovery of her diary: 'The title on the cover read **The Diary of Laura Perryman**.... With the book there was an envelope. I opened it and read.' And so the story begins.

Impersonal narration is written in the third person and can be from the viewpoint of an omniscient narrator who has complete access to the thoughts and feelings of all of the characters. As it is impossible for one person truly to know the innermost thoughts of another, attempts at full omniscience can lack credibility. It is more usual for an author to opt for limited omniscience in which the third-person narration reveals the point of view of one or two characters. Often the viewpoint of one character will be privileged above the others. In *The Lion, The Witch and the Wardrobe* by C.S. Lewis it is Lucy's point of view that is dominant, although we see some parts of the story from other perspectives. For example, it is through Edmund's eyes as well as the narrator's that we first see the White Witch.

Contemporary fiction often employs multiple viewpoints. In Anthony Browne's *Voices in the Park,* four characters tell their version of events when they meet in the park. The illustrations carry a viewpoint too and it is interesting to notice that the pictures do not necessarily carry the same point of view as the accompanying words. The reader can detect an authorial point of view that is different to the viewpoint of the characters.

NARRATIVE FICTION: GENERIC FEATURES

Features	NLS Framework	Prompt Questions
CHARACTER **Participants in the story** • **human** • **animal** • **other e.g. monster, alien** **Character presentation**	• Identify and discuss main and recurring characters, evaluate their behaviour, justify views (Y3 t2 *T3*) • Discuss: characters' feelings, behaviour e.g. fair or unreasonable, brave or foolish, relationships (Y3 t3 *T5*) • Identify the main characteristics of the key characters, drawing on the text to justify views, and using the information to predict actions (Y4 t1 *T2*) • Compare and evaluate a novel with film/TV version looking at the treatment of character (Y6 t1 *T1*)	• Which character did you feel closest to in this story? Why? • Which character did you find most interesting? Why? • Did you dislike any of the characters in this story? • Were you reminded of anyone you know by the characters in this story? • Do any words or phrases help to build a picture of this character? • Do you learn about this character from their appearance, what they say or what they do? • Did your opinion of this character change while you were reading?

NARRATIVE FICTION: GENERIC FEATURES

Commentary

In literature the term **character** means a participant in a story, whether human or non-human. We might talk about **character development**, by which we mean the extent to which a character grows and changes in the duration of the story. Children's fiction is often concerned with the growth of a child character into maturity or significant steps taken towards independence.

Characters are presented in literature through a variety of ways, for example through

- description, appearance
- action
- thought and speech
- placement in a specific setting
- style, language, vocabulary choice
- assessment and comment made by other characters
- the author's personal assessment and comment.

Consider the techniques these authors have used to convey character:

The house shook:

Wrapped in her quilt Meg shook.

She wasn't usually afraid of weather. It's not just the weather she thought. It's the weather on top of everything else. On top of me. On top of Meg Murray doing everything wrong.

School. School was all wrong. She'd been dropped down to the lowest section in her grade. That morning one of her teachers had said crossly, 'Really, Meg, I don't understand how a child with parents as brilliant as yours are supposed to be can be such a poor student. If you don't manage to do a little better, you'll have to stay back next year.'

Madeleine L'Engle, *A Wrinkle in Time*

In the first extract we learn little about Meg's appearance but a lot about her mood. Repetition of words and phrases (*shook, On top of*) combined with some very short staccato sentences (*School. School was all wrong.*) creates a picture of an oppressed and unhappy girl. The weather is a reflection of Meg's inner feelings; a literary convention called the **pathetic fallacy**. The third-person narrator is privileged with knowledge of Meg's feelings; this is Meg as if viewed from within, so external description is limited. There is some humour in this passage, which suggests a tendency to self-dramatisation, particularly as Meg plays back her teacher's words in her head.

His hair was tawny, his eyes black and deep-set in a pale, arrogant face. Though of excellent quality, his garments had seen much wear and his cloak was purposely draped to hide his threadbare attire. The cloak itself, Taran saw, had been neatly and painstakingly mended. He sat aside a roan mare, a lean and nervous steed speckled red and yellow, with a long, narrow head, whose expression was as ill-tempered as her master's.

Lloyd Alexander, *The Black Cauldron*

In contrast the second extract focuses largely on the description of the character's appearance and the reader can already begin to detect something about the likely personal qualities of this man. This is achieved partly through the use of adjectives which provide direct comment (*arrogant, ill-tempered*) but also through the objects that are associated with him (the cloak that has been painstakingly mended suggests that this is a man who does not place value on material possessions). There is a suggestion of pride in the manner in which the man tries 'to hide his threadbare attire'. The description of his hair colour (*tawny*) might conjure up a picture of a tawny owl, birds that are associated with wisdom and sharp vision.

NARRATIVE FICTION: GENERIC FEATURES

Features	NLS Framework	Prompt Questions
SUBJECT and THEME	• Identify typical story themes, e.g. trials and forfeits, good over evil, weak or strong, wise over foolish (Y3 t2 *T2*) • Review a range of stories, identifying, e.g. themes (Y4 t2 *T8*) • Identify social, moral or cultural issues in stories (Y4 t3 *T1*) • Discuss/write critically about an issue or dilemma raised in a story, explaining the problem, alternative courses of action and evaluating the writer's solution (Y4 t3 *T8*) • Be familiar with the work of some established authors, explain preference in terms of e.g. theme (Y6 t1 *T4*)	• Can you suggest some words to summarise what this story means to you? • Does this story remind you of any personal experience/something that has happened to you? • Does this story have a message? Do you know any other stories that have a similar message?

NARRATIVE FICTION: GENERIC FEATURES

Commentary

Subject and theme are words that describe what the story is about. The **subject** deals with what happens, and to whom, but the **theme** is a central idea that unifies the story. In Maurice Sendak's *Where the Wild Things Are,* the subject of the story is Max's unruly behaviour and subsequent punishment. Following a tantrum Max is sent to his room to cool down and there he fantasises/dreams about the wild things. However it is possible to go beyond the surface reading of this book and detect an underlying theme, which might be described as the psychological manifestation of Max's aggression. In Susan Hill's *Beware Beware*, the subject is a young girl who escapes from the watchful gaze of her mother and sets out to explore the wood at the very edge of her garden. The theme of this story might be identified as growth from dependence to independence. The subject of a book may be deceptively simple and yet have a profound theme, as is the case with Eric Carle's *Draw Me A Star*, which can be enjoyed by children at the foundation stage but still provide food for thought for readers in Year 6 and beyond. This complexity of theme is one of the reasons that picture books should continue to be part of children's reading experience long after they have 'learnt to read'.

Explicit themes are directly revealed in the text. In Margaret Shaw's *Walking the Maze*, Annice observes: 'The trouble with books ... is that books change people. The trouble is that you are never quite the same person at the end of a book as you were at the beginning.' Other themes are **implicit**, such as the example from *Where the Wild Things Are* described above. Comparing two books that have similar themes but different subjects can help to reveal to the young reader the deeper, underlying theme. Picture books provide an excellent means of achieving this objective as the entire narrative can be read/viewed in one session. Furthermore, as picture book themes are often challenging and complex, they can profitably be used with the most able readers in Year 6.

Some commonly occurring themes in children's fiction:

- facing and overcoming fear (Helen Cooper *The Bear Under the Stairs,* Anthony Browne *The Tunnel)*
- good versus evil (J.K. Rowling *Harry Potter and the Goblet of Fire)*
- coping with bereavement (Susan Varley *Badger's Parting Gifts)*
- acquisition of wisdom (Philip Pullman *The Firework-maker's Daughter)*
- growth from dependence to independence (*Hansel and Gretel)*
- self and selflessness (Louisa May Alcott *Little Women)*
- nature and civilisation (Jeannie Baker *Window,* Colin Thompson *The Paradise Garden)*
- freedom in the power of the imagination (Colin Thompson *The Paradise Garden)*
- abandonment (Cynthia Voigt *Homecoming, Hansel and Gretel)*
- secrets (Berlie Doherty *White Peak Farm,* Ann Cassidy *The Hidden Child)*
- heroism or bravery (Michael Coleman *Weirdo's War)*
- insight into different cultures and cultural values (Gaye Hicylmaz *The Frozen Waterfall)*
- nature of family life, responsibility (Anne Fine *The Book of the Banshee, Goggle Eyes)*
- exploration of interpersonal relationships (Helen Cooper *Pumpkin Soup)*
- exploration of intergenerational relationships (Philippe Dupsaquier *Sunday with Grandpa,* Philippa Pearce *Tom's Midnight Garden).*

NARRATIVE FICTION: GENERIC FEATURES

Features	NLS Framework	Prompt Questions
STYLE (1) **Vocabulary** **Sentence structure** **Figurative language** **Patterned language** **Descriptive language** **Reflective language** **Tense** **Tone**	• Investigate styles of traditional story language – collect examples e.g. openings and endings (Y3 t2 *T1*) • Refer to significant aspects of the text, e.g. opening etc., and know how language is used to create these (Y3 t3 *T2*) • Understand how the use of expressive and descriptive language can create moods, arouse expectations, build tension, describe attitudes or emotions (Y4 t2 *T4*) • Experiment with alternative ways of opening a story, e.g. description, action or dialogue (Y5 t1 *T11*) • Explore similarities and differences between oral and written storytelling (Y5 t2 *T3*) • Investigate features of different fiction genres (Y5 t2 *T9*) • Understand the differences between literal and figurative language (Y5 t2 *T10*) • Describe and evaluate the style of an individual writer (Y6 t3 *T1*)	• Was there anything you particularly liked or disliked about the way in which this story was told? • How did the author try to capture your interest in the first four lines of this story? • Which words/phrases have been used to develop an atmosphere of suspense/mystery? • Are any words or phrases repeated? What effect does this create?

NARRATIVE FICTION: GENERIC FEATURES

Commentary

Fictional style is determined by a number of factors including:

- **lexical choices**: complexity and range of vocabulary
- use of **figurative language** such as simile, metaphor and personification
- **sentence types**: grammatical structures, repetition, sentence length, characteristic phrases, complexity
- **descriptive** elements and the balance between description and moving the plot forward
- balance of **reflection** or **action**
- **dialogue**: the amount and manner of its presentation, such as the use of colloquial effect or dialect features

Vocabulary

When discussing text suitability it is often the complexity of vocabulary that is regarded as the most obvious indicator of text difficulty. Before dismissing books with polysyllabic words as necessarily difficult, however, it is worth remembering that vocabulary is not the most significant factor in determining the textual difficulty. The supporting context in which new vocabulary is used needs to be taken into account. Many parents will testify to their children picking up words such as 'soporific' and 'affronted' having been introduced to the original versions of Beatrix Potter's *Tale of Peter Rabbit* and *Tale of Tom Kitten*. In fact, over-simplification of vocabulary may make a text more difficult to understand if it means that the context is insufficiently described.

See also notes headed 'Diction' in the poetry section (p. 161).

Figurative language

See the discussion in the poetry section (pp. 158–9).

Description and vocabulary choice

Words are to the writer what paint is to the painter. Effective description is dependent on selecting exactly the right word.

Whatever you want to say, there is only one word that will express it, one verb to make it move, one adjective to qualify. You must seek that word, that verb, and that adjective, and never be satisfied with approximations.

Gustav Flaubert

Good writers select precise verbs. Instead of *walk* they might choose *amble*, *saunter*, *step*, *shuffle*, *march*, etc. While adverbs modify verbs, their use can sometimes diminish the impact of the verb. For example, compare the following:

Colin ran down the road extremely quickly.
Colin sprinted down the road.

Which of these is the better description?

However, an over-emphasis on strong verbs is not a hallmark of good writing. Too much exaggeration destroys the reader's belief; there are times when simple choices such as walk or said are best words.

NARRATIVE FICTION: GENERIC FEATURES

Features	NLS Framework	Prompt Questions
STYLE (2) **Narration of thought and speech**	• Investigate how dialogue is presented in stories e.g. through statements, exclamations; how paragraphing is used to create dialogue (Y3 t1 *T2*) • Experiment with alternative ways of opening a story e.g. description, action or dialogue (Y5 t1 *T11*) • Write in the style of the author, e.g. writing additional dialogue (Y5 t3 *W9*)	• Compare the way in which different authors write dialogue. • Does the author tell you what the character is thinking or do you have to work this out from other clues and hints?
Style and genre	• Investigate features of different fiction genres (Y5 t2 *T9*)	• Can you tell from the first paragraph what kind of story we are reading? What are the clues that help you to identify the type of story?

NARRATIVE FICTION: GENERIC FEATURES

Commentary

Narration of speech and thought

It has been suggested that young readers like books that contain dialogue as this assists the reading process for them. In fact the degree of textual difficulty can be influenced by the way in which speech and thought are presented. Basically there are four forms of presentation:

Tagged: speech or thought is presented with a tag (e.g. *she said, he thought, they argued*).
Free: speech or thought does not possess a tag.
Direct: *shows* the reader what has been said or thought: *I have to go.*
Indirect: *tells* the reader what has been said or thought: *She said she would have to go. He thought it was time to leave the party.*

The level of control that an author has over the reader's response is partly reflected in the way in which speech and thought are presented. The greatest control is exercised by using indirect tagged speech: *She whispered quietly to the prince that she would have to go.* This gives the reader a lot of information and consequently places limits on interpretation. Direct free speech (e.g. '*I have to go*') provides the least information so the reader has to work harder at interpretation: in order to work out how this is said and to whom, the reader has to use the surrounding context. Usually speech is presented in direct-tagged mode while thought is presented in indirect-tagged mode. To present thought directly is the most artificial representation as one person cannot know precisely what another is thinking.

Style and genre

Different types of narrative fiction produce writing with specific stylistic features. Often it is possible to tell from a few lines what type of story you are reading. Take, for instance, the following story openings. What kind of story do you think each of them is? What clues help you to identify the genre?

Once upon a time there was a widow and she had three daughters and they said to her that they would go to seek their fortune.

We'd gone right through the school collecting the teachers' tea money and had got to the canteen door when Danny waved the ten pound note at me.

You were probably able to identify without too much difficulty that the first opening is from a traditional folk tale. First of all there is the use of the conventional aperture *Once upon a time*, which underpins the story's timeless quality. The characters do not appear to be named; the woman is simply 'a widow'. This is typical of the traditional tale; she represents a role rather than a real widow. You may also have noted that folk tales often seem to have patterns of three: three bears, three little pigs, three wishes, etc. We know from our experiences of such stories that an event will occur three times but on the third occasion the pattern will be broken, this is the most economical way of emphasising the moral point in the story. Typically this extract includes examples of archaic language *to seek their fortune*; in contemporary terms this might be expressed as 'make money'.

In the second example the vocabulary is recognised as belonging to the semantic field 'school' – school, teachers, tea money, canteen – so we can identify the setting and possibly we might anticipate that this extract is from a 'school story'. It is written in the first person and the style is informal – the contraction *we'd* and the verb choice *gone* signals an oral voice. We have probably identified that the speaker is a child and we may be wondering what connection is to be made between the tea money and the ten pound note. The extract is from Gene Kemp's *The Turbulent Term of Tyke Tiler.*

POETRY

Features	NLS Framework	Prompt Questions
FORM **Rhyme**	• Distinguish between rhyming and non-rhyming poetry and comment on the impact of layout (Y3 t1 *T7*) • Identify patterns of rhyme and verse in poetry (Y4 t2 *T7*) • Understand the following terms and identify them in poems: verse, chorus, couplet, stanza, rhyme, rhythm, alliteration (Y4 t3 *T4*) • Describe how a poet does or does not use rhyme (e.g. every alternate line, rhyming couplets (Y4 t3 *T3*) • Analyse and compare poetic style, use of forms of significant poets; consider the impact of full rhymes, half rhymes, internal rhymes and other sound patterns (Y5 t1 *T7*)	• Do you hear any repeating patterns in this poem? • Can you predict what word the poet might have used here …?

POETRY

Commentary

The form of poetry is its shape and structure rather than the content. However, form and content are inextricably linked and although it is possible to examine them separately, poetry discussions with children should embrace both. When discussing the shape and pattern of a poem we might also talk about the effect the structure has on the way we feel or think about the subject and theme.

A secondary meaning of form is used to describe the genre to which a poem belongs e.g. sonnet, cinquain.

Rhyme

Rhyme is the patterning of sound and creates a range of different moods and effects in poetry. Playful rhyming can arouse pleasure in the sounds of the language. Very young children often display this pleasure when they generate their own nonsense rhymes. A strong rhyming pattern increases predictability and can provide comforting endings while the introduction of half rhymes can make a poem sound wistful or sad. An unexpected break in a regular rhyming pattern can create dissonance and unease. The ingenuity of rhyming is an important feature of some comic verse where the humour is derived from the skill and contrivance of the poet. Look at the rhyme in the following examples:

Jack and Jill
Went up the hill

One for the master, one for the dame
One for the little boy who lives down the lane

In these well-known nursery rhymes *Jill* and *hill* are full rhymes. As they occur at the end of the line they are simply called end rhymes. *Dame* and *lane* have the same vowel phoneme but do not rhyme fully and are therefore called half rhymes. When a rhyme occurs within the line it is called an internal rhyme, as can be seen in the following example of an internal half rhyme from Sylvia Plath's 'Mushrooms':

Overnight, very
Whitely, discreetly,
Very quietly

Two successive rhyming lines of poetry are called couplets. Shakespeare often used a rhyming couplet with a strong closure to signal the end of a scene:

Away, and mock the time with fairest show:
False face must hide what false heart doth know.
Macbeth Act I scene vii

Alliteration is another form of sound pattern in which an initial consonant is repeated. Walter de la Mare uses this technique to create a palpable silence in his poem 'The Listeners':

The silence surged softly backward,
When the plunging hoofs were gone.

Other sound patterns such as consonance (when the repeated consonants are not in the initial position) and assonance, repeated vowels, may be used.

An example of alliteration and consonance can be found In Wilfred Owen's 'Anthem for Doomed Youth'. In the following lines the repeated consonants mimic the sound of machine gun fire.

Only the stuttering rifles' rapid rattle
Can patter out their hasty orisons.

Owen's poem clearly shows the significance of sound patterns in intensifying the poem's meaning.

When poets use words similar to the sounds associated with them, as in the above example, this is called onomatopoeia. The effect is often created by the use of alliteration for example *drip-drop, drip-drop*.

Listening to the effects created by the patterning of sound and discussing the impact these have on the tone and mood of the poem is more important than learning the terminology attached to them.

POETRY

Features	NLS Framework	Prompt Questions
FORM **Rhythm**	• Understand terms and identify them in poems; rhythm (Y4 t3 *T4*) • Clap out and count the syllables in each line of regular poetry (Y4 t3 *T5*) • Recognise how poets manipulate words for their quality of sound e.g. rhythm (Y6 t2 *T3*) • Analyse how messages, moods, feelings and attitudes are conveyed in poetry (Y6 t2 *T5*)	• Can you hear any patterns in this poem when we clap the rhythm? • Can you predict the rhythm of the last line if I clap the first three lines? (Strong regular rhythms in traditional ballads, for example.)

POETRY

Commentary

Rhythm and metre

The word rhythm derives from Greek and means 'flow'. Rhythm elicits a basic response in human beings; feet start tapping to the Irish jig, bodies sway to the Reggae beat and a quick two-step requires a march. The rhythm of a poem is the way it flows and is determined by the occurrence of stressed and unstressed syllables and their duration.

While many poems do not rhyme, all poetry makes some use of rhythm and it is this aspect of the poem that frequently contributes to a poem's appeal. For instance, John Masefield's 'Sea Fever' or Robert Louis Stevenson's 'View From A Railway Carriage' are frequently quoted as being among the most memorable poems of childhood. Both of these poems have strong rhythms and even when all of the words are not remembered the rhythm might be hummed.

I must down to the seas again, to the lonely sea and sky,
And all I ask is a tall ship and a star to steer her by
John Masefield

Faster than fairies faster than witches,
Bridges and houses, hedges and ditches
Robert Louis Stevenson

When a poet uses regular patterns of stressed and unstressed syllables this is called metre. The most common metre in English poetry is the iambic metre.

An iambic foot comprises an unstressed syllable followed by a stressed syllable. Often Shakespeare's verse is written with five iambic feet in each line: dee-dum, dee-dum, dee-dum, dee-dum, dee-dum. This rhythmic pattern is called iambic pentameters (five iambic feet). Can you detect this rhythm in the following:

Shall I compare thee to a summer's day?
Thou art more lovely and more temperate:
Rough winds do shake the darling buds of May,
And summer's lease hath all too short a date;
William Shakespeare, Sonnet 18

When verse contains a strong rhythm but no rhyme, as in the following example, it is called blank verse.

I am that merry wanderer of the night.
I jest to Oberon, and make him smile
When I a fat and bean-fed horse beguile,
Neighing in likeness of a filly foal;
A Midsummer Night's Dream Act II scene i

Changes in rhythm draw attention to changes in mood, attitude or ideas.

Syllabic forms

Some forms of verse and poetry are constructed according to the number of syllables in each line. The best known is the Japanese haiku but there are other syllable-based forms, including cinquains, tanka and renga.

POETRY

Features	NLS Framework	Prompt Questions

FIGURATIVE LANGUAGE	• Understand the use of figurative language in poetry and prose; compare poetic phrasing with narrative/descriptive examples (Y4 t2 *T5*)
	• Understand the difference between literal and figurative language, e.g. through discussing the effects of imagery in poetry (and prose) (Y5 t2 *T10*)
	• Recognise how poets manipulate words:
	    for their connotations
	    for multiple layers of meaning, e.g. through figurative language, ambiguity (Y6 t2 *T3*)
		• Describe/draw the pictures that the poem creates in your mind

POETRY

Commentary

Unlike literal language, figurative language uses figures of speech such as metaphor, simile and idiom. Some uses of figurative language are in common use and have become idiomatic, for example: *She flew down the stairs. He is as cool as a cucumber.*

Generally we would not regard these uses of figurative language as poetic, which is determined by original forms of expression that enable the reader to see things from a fresh perspective.

Often in poetry there is a concentrated use of figurative language, which enables the poet to convey layers of meaning in few words. Jerome Bruner referred to this compression in poetry as 'semantic squeeze'. In poetry, carefully selected words prompt the reader to conjure up images drawn from their bank of personal experiences and memories.

One of the most common figures of speech is the simile, which explicitly compares one thing to another using the words *like* and *as*:

I wandered lonely as a cloud
That floats on high o'er vales and hills.
William Wordsworth, 'Daffodils'

The simile works on more than one level so that several potential meanings can simultaneously be brought to mind. For example, by comparing himself to an object in nature the poet suggests that he is at one with the landscape. At the same time the visual image of a lone cloud in a vast sky depicts the loneliness that is referred to in this line.

Metaphor also compares one thing to another but omits a linking word (*as, like*):

The road was a ribbon of moonlight
Over the purple moor
Alfred Noyes, 'The Highwayman'

Sometimes the metaphor is extended throughout the poem as in Ted Hughes's 'The Thought Fox', in which the fox is a metaphor for the writing process. Another example is William Dunlop's 'Landscape as Werewolf', which likens the fells to the wolves that once used to roam the hills and forests.

Personification is the attribution of human qualities to inanimate objects or abstract ideas. The gendering of objects is often conventional. Death is most frequently depicted as male, while spring is usually female. The sun is male and the moon female, for example in Christina Rossetti's poem 'Is the Moon Tired?'.

Is the Moon tired? She looks so pale
Within her misty veil;
She scales the sky from east to west,
And takes no rest

POETRY

Features	NLS Framework	Prompt Questions
LANGUAGE **Word play**	• Compare types of humour e.g. word play (Y3 t3 *T6*) • Select, prepare, read aloud and recite by heart poetry that plays with language or entertains (Y3 t3 *T7*) • Investigate and collect different examples of word play relating form to meaning (Y5 t1 *T8*)	• Do you notice anything special or unusual about the words the poet has used?

Features	NLS Framework	Prompt Questions
LANGUAGE **Vocabulary**	• Read aloud and recite poems; discuss choice of words and phrases that describe and create impact, e.g. adjectives, powerful and expressive verbs (Y3 t1 *T6*) • Identify clues which suggest poems are older, e.g. language use, vocabulary, archaic words (Y4 t2 *T6*) • Recognise how poets manipulate words (Y6 t2 *T3*) • Analyse how messages, moods, feelings and attitudes are conveyed in poetry (Y6 t2 *T5*)	• Are there any words or phrases that you particularly like? • What do you feel when you read this poem? Sad? Angry? • Are there any words or phrases that stick in your mind?

POETRY

Commentary

A pun is a play on words often to humorous effect. So for example in *Romeo and Juliet*, Mercutio's final words are:

Ask for me tomorrow
And you shall find me a grave man.
                    Romeo and Juliet Act III scene i

The humour is dependent on both meanings of the word *grave* being simultaneously called up. In spite of the pun, the mood in this scene is dark and foreboding, illustrating the point that humour is not exclusively concerned with describing funny situations and can play a part in reinforcing tragedy.

Jaqueline Brown's poem 'Have you Ever Thought' is lighter but also derives its humour from the different meanings of words:

A comb has teeth but can't bite,
A shoe has a tongue but can't talk

Another form of pun is to be found in Lewis Carroll's pun 'Laughing and Grief' (for Latin and Greek) and poetry collection *Sadderday and Funday* (Saturday and Sunday) which rely on a similarity in sound rather than two meanings of the same word.

Ambiguity and word play

Sometimes syntax allows ambiguity to exist. In the following example humour is dependent on the verb being unexpectedly applied to both elephants and inanimate lamp-posts (though our experience of this type of joke might lead us to anticipate this outcome).

Can an elephant jump higher than a lamp-post?
Yes: lamp-posts can't jump.

Commentary

Diction is the term used to refer to vocabulary choice. In the eighteenth century an artificial diction, influenced by neoclassicism, was preferred but by the beginning of the nineteenth century poets were beginning to talk about the virtue of using more commonplace language including colloquialism, though this was not often achieved in practice. In the mid-twentieth century Wallace Stevens introduced the concept of the 'anti-poetic' based on the conviction that there did not have to be anything special or particular about the language of poetry.

When we read verse from the eighteenth and nineteenth centuries we can detect words that are no longer in common usage as in the next example, where *doth* is an archaic form of the present singular *does*.

How doth the little busy bee
Improve each shining hour
                    Isaac Watts, 'Against Idleness and Mischief'

Isaac Watts's poem was published in 1715. However, such use of archaic language does not necessarily mean that the poem is very old. For instance Walter de la Mare's 'The Listeners' includes the following lines:

Never the least stir made the listeners,
        Though every word he spake
Fell echoing through the shadowiness of the still house
        From the one man left awake:

Though de la Mare uses the archaic form of the past tense of the verb to speak and other words that are no longer in common usage (*spake* instead of spoke, *dwelt* instead of lived, *smote* instead of struck) the poem was actually published in 1912. The diction of 'The Listeners' creates the impression of an earlier age and is a reflection of de la Mare's interest in the old ballads and the romantic tradition of writing for children.

It is interesting to compare the diction in the above poems to contemporary examples such as James Berry's 'Girls Can We Educate We Dads?' and Michael Rosen's collection *Wouldn't You Like to Know.*

NON-FICTION TEXT: GENERIC FEATURES

Features	NLS Framework	Prompt Questions
STRUCTURAL ORGANISERS	• To understand the distinction between fact and fiction; to use the terms *fact*, *fiction* and *non-fiction* appropriately (Y3 t1 *T17*) • To notice differences in the style and structure of fiction and non-fiction writing (Y3 t1 *T18*) • To locate information using contents, index, headings, subheadings, page numbers, bibliographies (Y3 t1 *T19*) • To compare the way information is presented (Y3 t1 *T20*) • To appraise a non-fiction book for its contents and usefulness by scanning headings, contents list, etc. (Y4 t2 *T15*) • To locate information confidently and efficiently through using contents, indexes, sections, headings (Y5 t2 *T17*) • To note how authors record and acknowledge their sources (Y5 t2 *T18*)	• What's the purpose of this book? Why would you read it? • Does this book have a central character? • What makes it different from a story? • Does this [non-fiction] book have chapters? • How has the author organised the material in this book? • What could you find out from this book? • How do you know if the information is accurate? What kind of expertise does the author have? How do you know? • Compare the contents page of a fiction and a non-fiction book: what do you notice? • Look at the bibliography: why might this be useful?

Features	NLS Framework	Prompt Questions
HEADINGS SUBHEADINGS	• To locate information using contents, index, headings, subheadings, page numbers, bibliographies (Y3 t1 *T19*) • To identify features of non-fiction texts in print and IT, e.g. headings, lists, bullet-points, captions, which support the reader in gaining information effectively (Y4 t2 *T17*) • To scan texts on print or screen to find useful headings (Y4 t2 *T17*) • To locate information confidently and efficiently through using contents, indexes, sections, headings (Y5 t2 *T17*)	• Where could you find out about … in this book? • Is there any other way? What's the quickest way? • How many levels of headings and subheadings does this book have? Are they factual or do they ask questions? • Do you take notice of the headings when you scan?

NON-FICTION TEXT: GENERIC FEATURES

Commentary

The purpose of structural organisers is to enable information to be located and to remind the reader of relevant concepts. Structural organisers which distinguish non-fiction from fiction text include:

Cover: the title is factual and the back cover will often summarise the book's contents briefly.

Contents: chapter headings are informative.

Chapter headings and subheadings throughout the text organise the material into separate sections; there may be a number of different levels of headings, sometimes marked numerically (e.g. section 1, 1.1, 1.1.1 … 2, 2.1 …).

Summaries or abstracts at the start or end of sections or chapters.

Glossary: to define specialist terms.

Index: to locate information; lists pages in ascending order; may have subheadings under main entries.

Bibliography: to enable the reader to do further research; shows where the writer got their information.

Preface: may summarise the contents and orient the reader.

Specialist terms: may be highlighted in the text, not for emphasis but to attract attention to them and remind the reader of related concepts.

References: where the author acknowledges the sources used.

Acknowledgements (sometimes called credits): where the author acknowledges the source of material copied here, often photographs but could be text.

Appendix: for additional material. Not often found in children's books.

Commentary

A distinctive feature of information texts, headings and subheadings may be marked typographically: by size, emphasis, colour and typeface, or with bullet points. Alternatively they may be numbered to indicate importance.

How many levels of headings are useful? How conscious is the reader of headings and subheadings? Are they informative or do they attempt to engage active reading by posing a question e.g. *What makes clouds?* How accurately do they describe the material that follows? Are plain, factual headings easier to use than catchy, quirky ones? Or do they distract?

NON-FICTION TEXT: GENERIC FEATURES

Features	NLS Framework	Prompt Questions
INDEX	• To locate information using contents, index, headings, subheadings, page numbers, bibliographies (Y3 t1 *T19*) • To scan indexes, directories and IT sources etc. to locate information quickly and accurately (Y3 t3 *T17*) • To locate information confidently and efficiently through using contents, indexes, sections, headings (Y5 t2 *T17*)	• What's the difference between the index and the contents? • If you want to find out about ... how could you do it? Where would you start? • What's the best place to look for information about ...? • If you can't find information in the contents, where else might you look? • If there isn't an entry in the index, what might you do to find out about ...? • How could I use the search engine to find information about ... ? • Why are the sites found organised in this order? Why are 'hot links' useful?

Features	NLS Framework	Prompt Questions
GLOSSARY	• To use glossaries (Y2 t2 *T16*) • To understand that glossaries give definitions and explanations (Y2 t2 *T17*)	• Compare the definitions of ... given in the glossary of at least two books. Which one is clearer? • When you were doing research about ... were there any words that you looked up in the glossary? Was the glossary helpful?

NON-FICTION TEXT: GENERIC FEATURES

Indexes are organised in alphabetical order of entries with page numbers in ascending order. Sometimes entries have subheadings, e.g.

gods 8, 14, 16, 20, 32
    Jupiter 14
    Mars 16

A good index only directs the reader to helpful references, not to every mention of the entry in the text. Indexes that have been constructed by mechanically recording every entry are unhelpful and demotivating to the student who is searching for a particular piece of information. For example, suppose that a pupil is studying earthquakes and wants to know what the earth's crust is. *Earthquakes* (Kingscourt: 1999) has five references to crust in the index; the first four are informative but the fifth refers to 'the grating movement of the plates has caused a weblike series of faults and cracks in the crust.' A learner in Key Stage 2, looking for information to complete a sentence starting 'The crust is...' would not find this very helpful. On the other hand, *Our Violent Earth: Earthquakes* (Hodder Wayland: 2001) does not have an entry for crust in the index but has a good definition in the section What Causes Earthquakes?: 'the crust, made up of huge slabs of rock called tectonic plates.'

A glossary defines specialist terms. A good definition should be able to be substituted within the text and would make sense. The problem with a glossary is that the author cannot be sure of the reader's prior knowledge and may assume some familiarity with other terms. An unhelpful glossary is one where the definition offered needs further clarification because the terms used in the definition are not familiar. If the reader needs to define more than one term within a definition, their comprehension of the passage is likely to be seriously impaired.

Sometimes glossaries seem to give different amounts of information. Compare these definitions of the Mercalli scale: 'A scale that measures the amount of shaking during an earthquake' (*Earthquakes*, Kingscourt: 1999); 'a way of measuring how much damage an earthquake causes' (*Our Violent Earth: Earthquakes*, Hodder Wayland: 2001). And the Richter scale: 'a scale that measures the amount of energy released by an earthquake. It is expressed in numerals between 1 and 9' (*Earthquakes*, Kingscourt: 1999); 'A way of measuring the strength of an earthquake' (*Our Violent Earth: Earthquakes*, Hodder Wayland: 2001). It is a useful piece of research to compare any two terms in two different glossaries and see how they differ.

NON-FICTION TEXT: GENERIC FEATURES

Features	NLS Framework	Prompt Questions
REGISTER	The NLS does not explicitly refer to register. However, the concept of register is implied in all references which compare different kinds of non-fiction texts: • to read examples of letters written for a range of purposes and ways of addressing different audiences – formal/informal (Y3 t3 *T16*) • to identify different types of text e.g. their content, structure, vocabulary, style, layout and purpose (Y4 t1 *T16*) • to distinguish between biography and autobiography (Y6 t1 *T11*) • to read and understand examples of official language and its characteristic features e.g. through discussing consumer information, legal documents (Y6 t2 *T17*) • to identify key features of impersonal formal language e.g. the present tense, the passive voice and discuss when and why they are used (Y6 t3 *T16*) • to review a range of non-fiction text types and their characteristics, discussing when a writer might choose to write in a given style and form (Y6 t3 *T19*)	• Do you think the letter-writer is a friend of the person who will receive it? Why/why not? • What words/phrases have been used which give you clues that this is a formal letter? • Who wrote the book about Mandela's life? How would it be different if Mandela had written it himself? • Highlight the words and phrases that you find in formal documents. Which ones wouldn't you use if you were writing to a friend? • Why has the author set out the instructions like this? Could they have been written any other way? • How could this be made to sound more friendly and informal? • How could this be made to sound more formal or serious?

NON-FICTION TEXT: GENERIC FEATURES

Commentary

Register refers to the style of the text. It encompasses the content or purpose of the text, the way the channel of communication affects the language used and how the social distance between author and reader is marked. It ranges on a continuum from formal to informal.

Informal registers use colloquial language; formal registers use more archaic language and tend to be used in highly specialist texts. The concept of register can be applied to fiction as well as non-fiction texts. The advantage of this concept is that it includes field (the content or subject matter), mode (the channel of communication and associated features e.g. spoken or written) and tenor (the social distance between author and reader) and enables us to explore how they relate.

Neate (1992) arranges information texts along the formal–informal continuum, with Identification key guides and Historical key guides as examples of the most formal register, biographical texts and Learn and do books at a midpoint, and narrative information texts at the informal end. Letters, too, can be arranged along the continuum of register, from informal notes to close friends to very formal letters addressed to unknown recipients in organisations. While every curriculum area will have its own register, some texts disregard the conventional relations to produce anomalous texts that cross the usual boundaries. Examples of anomalous texts might be narrative information books or docudrama on TV.

More formal styles assume the writer is an expert who imparts authoritative knowledge to the reader. By using an impersonal style the author appears absent. A formal style of writing may use short, dense, elliptical sentences with much specialist terminology. Less formal styles will be more descriptive and may address the reader directly, e.g. 'When you walk through a fog, you are really walking through a cloud.'

Littlefair (1993) provides a clear discussion of register, genre and associated topics.

NON-FICTION TEXT: GENERIC FEATURES

Features	NLS Framework	Prompt Questions
SPECIALIST TECHNICAL VOCABULARY **JARGON**	• To notice differences in the style ... of non-fiction writing (Y3 t1 *T18*) • To read a range of explanatory texts investigating and noting features of impersonal style e.g. technical vocabulary (Y5 t2 *T15*)	• Does this sound complicated? • Could you write this in simpler terms? • What words and phrases tell you that the author is describing the anatomy of an insect? Why did he use *thorax* and *abdomen* and not *body*?

Features	NLS Framework	Prompt Questions

COHESION
 	
CONNECTIVES
	• To investigate through reading and writing how words and phrases signal time sequences e.g. *first, then, after, meanwhile, from, where* (Y3 t3 *S6*)
	• To identify the features of recounted texts such as sports reports, diaries, police reports, including:
	    – Introduction to set the scene
	    – Chronological sequence
	    – Use of connectives e.g. *first, next, once* (Y5 t1 *T21*)
		• Highlight the words that tell you which order to follow (e.g. first, then, after, finally). Why are these words useful to the reader?
		• What words indicate that some people think differently about this issue (e.g. however, although) or that there are different points of view (e.g. on the other hand)?
		• What are the main ideas in this paragraph and how are they related?

NON-FICTION TEXT: GENERIC FEATURES

Commentary

Specialist terms are used to describe key concepts with specific definitions. Sometimes these terms have a different meaning in popular usage, e.g. *volume*, *mass*, *gas*, *pressure*, *litter*, *nap*, *estate*, *habitat*, which can mislead the reader. It is important to ensure that children understand the definition of new terms but it may be very difficult to achieve this understanding as these may be precisely the concepts that the text is attempting to teach. Technical terms may be highlighted in the text with a different typeface, indicating that they are defined in the glossary. When text contains too many specialist terms, it becomes very dense and hard to follow: e.g. 'These simple molecules include glucose (from carbohydrate digestion), amino acids (from protein digestion) and fatty acids (from fat digestion).' It isn't easy to see how such a sentence could be simplified, although 'from eating sugar and starch' might have replaced the phrase 'from carbohydrate digestion'.

Another problem with specialist terms is how they are defined within the text. Sometimes authors will put a definition in parentheses e.g. 'Digestive juices are secreted (leak) from its walls.' As long as the reader knows that the words inside the brackets are substitutes for the previous word or phrase, this is helpful. However, more often the author uses *or,* which is a tricky word when the reader does not know whether it means 'different from' or 'the same as'. Here are two contrasting examples: 'The clusters can be cone-shaped *or* long and dangling…' (*or* means the alternative: either/or; there are two kinds of clusters); 'seeds with barbs, *or* hooks, catch on to animals' fur…' (*or* means *the same as*).

While specialist technical vocabulary may be unavoidable, jargon is an unnecessary use of uncommon words, e.g. *locate* when *find* would do, *inform* instead of *tell*, or *depict* instead of *show*. This simply makes the text sound pompous and less accessible. 'Offspring resemble their parents' could have been written as 'Children are like their parents'.

Commentary

Cohesion is a linguistic term referring to the internal unity of a text: how its parts relate together. Global cohesion refers to the overall organisation, which may be marked by headings and subheadings, while local cohesion depends on words that relate the ideas in a text together. A list does not have cohesion. Clauses in sentences and sentences in a paragraph are often related – causally (*because*, *as*), temporally (*before*, *after*, *then*, *finally*) or in other ways. *And* and *but* are simple connectives, whereas *however* and *furthermore* express more subtle relationships. A passage about an event or a process is likely to contain sentences which include words like *therefore, consequently, nevertheless, since, while, although, on account of* which qualify the relationship between statements. These words are often misunderstood by pupils, who tend to skip them when they read. Sometimes, thinking that simplification will help, authors leave out connectives altogether. However, a text composed of a number of short sentences can be harder to understand than one where the relationship between the events is explicitly described. It is important for teachers to make sure that the implicit relationships between processes or events are fully understood by pupils, especially where cohesive markers have been omitted.

Global cohesion can be explored by examining the information packed on to the page of some books. Some have a number of separate sections with disparate facts linked only loosely to the central focus.

NON-FICTION TEXT: GENERIC FEATURES

Features	NLS Framework	Prompt Questions
CHRONOLOGY **Narrative** **Sequence** **Non-narrative**	The NLS does not explicitly discuss narrative in information texts. It focuses mainly on sequenced texts: • To understand the difference between verbs in the 1st, 2nd and 3rd person … through – relating to different types of text, e.g. 3rd person for narrative, recounts (Y3 t2 *S10*) • To discuss the merits and limitations of particular instructional texts, including IT and other media texts, and to compare these with others where appropriate to give an overall evaluation (Y3 t2 *T13*) • How written instructions are organised e.g. lists, numbered points, diagrams with arrows, bullet points (Y3 t2 *T14*) • To identify the features of instructional texts including: setting out sequential stages clearly (Y4 t1 *T22*) • To identify the features of recounted texts such as sports reports … including chronological sequence (Y5 t1 *T21*) • To secure understanding of the features of non-chronological reports … mostly present tense (Y6 t1 *T13*)	• Is it easier to find information about … on the CD-ROM or in the book? Why? • How did you know which part to look at first? Was it clear? • How do the arrows on the diagram help you to understand the life-cycle of the butterfly? Could you tell the cycle as a story?

NON-FICTION TEXT: GENERIC FEATURES

Commentary

There are two kinds of chronology: **narrative** and **sequence**. Narrative refers to information ordered along the lines of a story, while sequence refers to information to be followed in a linear order, such as instructions. It is important for teachers to be aware that information books may incorporate some element of narrative.

Non-narrative texts: reference books; information books; expository text that describes, explains or sets out an argument. The majority of non-fiction information texts that children encounter in school will be non-narrative.

Narrative information books: Although many information books are organised non-chronologically, some use a narrative form. Examples would be 'information stories', biographies, autobiographies and diaries. In information stories written as narratives it may be hard for the reader to discern fact from fiction. Their purpose seems to be to inform but the author disguises this by using less specialist vocabulary and organising information around a central character – an animal, an insect, a tree, a historical person. Neate (1992) is critical of these books as they follow the structure of story books, with chapters, and contain no structural guiders or organisers to facilitate the retrieval of information. The appeal of the story is intended to make the information memorable and meaningful. Do they resemble good stories? Is there a plot? Does the reader empathise with the central character? Narrative information books are often used in Key Stage 1 (e.g. *I Know Where My Food Goes* by Jacqui Maynard, illustrated by Katherine McEwen, Walker Books: 2000).

As well as these, there are some books and series of hybrid texts, deliberately combining narrative with non-narrative. For example, Walker Books' 'Read and Wonder' series is described as 'picture books full of facts and feeling about the real world'; the feeling is conveyed through the fiction text which accompanies the non-fiction, distinguished from it by a different typeface. The non-fiction text uses technical terms, whereas the fiction text uses figurative and literary language. These hybrid texts provide good examples of the contrast between fact and fiction for children to compare. The language of the story is vivid and poetic, very different from the dry vocabulary of the information line. Compare 'Think of an eel. After years in the river he's slit-eyed and slimy and thick like a snake' with 'Eels feed mostly at night' (*Think of an Eel* by Karen Wallace, Walker Books: 1993). Books from this series would make a good contrast with conventional information books. For example, pupils could compare *Think of an Eel* with *Frog* by Stephen Savage (Wayland: 1994) or *Frogs and Toads* by Helen Riley (Wayland: 1991). The non-fiction books cover the predictable topics of habitat, reproduction, life-cycle, feeding habits, etc. Does *Think of an Eel* include the same information, but present it differently?

Sequentially ordered texts: all procedural writing which provides instructions to be followed is organised in a sequence. The sequence is critical to correct completion of the task. Recipes and instructions are ordered sequentially. The information can be presented visually as in the numbered sequences of diagrams that accompany DIY self-assembly kits. Every IKEA customer has experience of these!

NON-FICTION TEXT: GENERIC FEATURES

Features	NLS Framework	Prompt Questions
PERSPECTIVE	• To understand and use the terms fact and opinion and to begin to distinguish between the two in reading and other media (Y4 t1 *T19*) • To read, compare and evaluate examples of arguments and discussions, e.g. letters to press, articles, discussion of issues in books, e.g. environment, animal welfare (Y4 t3 *T16*) • From examples of persuasive writing, to investigate how style and vocabulary are used to convince the intended reader (Y4 t3 *T18*) • To evaluate advertisements for their impact, appeal and honesty (Y4 t3 *T19*) • To evaluate texts critically by comparing how different sources treat the same information (Y5 t2 *T19*) • To read and evaluate letters e.g. from newspapers or magazines, intended to inform, protest, complain, persuade, considering (i) how they are set out, (ii) how language is used e.g. to gain attention, respect, to manipulate (Y5 t3 *T12*) • Compare writing which informs and persuades, considering e.g. the deliberate use of ambiguity, half-truth, bias; how opinion can be disguised to seem like fact (Y5 t3 *T13*) • From reading, to collect and investigate use of persuasive devices (Y5 t3 *T15*) • To distinguish between biography and autobiography, distinguishing between implicit and explicit points of view and how these can differ (Y6 t1 *T11*) • To identify the features of balanced written arguments which e.g. signal personal opinion clearly (Y6 t2 *T16*)	• Which article/letter would most persuade you to change your mind? Why? • What words/phrases/questions/points were the most powerful in persuading you that hunting was wrong? • Has one author given information in their book that the other hasn't? What has been left out? Is it important? • Have the books/authors presented the information in different ways? Which is the most effective? Why? • Whose viewpoint is being presented here? Whose viewpoint is omitted? • What does the writer want to persuade you to think/do? • Who is this advert trying to persuade? • Who wrote this advert/article? • Why did they write it? • Can you tell what they think? How?
Features	NLS Framework	Prompt Questions
REFERENCE TEXTS	Children are encouraged to use dictionaries from Key Stage 1. The range of dictionaries referred to expands in Key Stage 2 to include rhyming dictionaries (Y4 t1), slang dictionaries (Y5 t3), etymological dictionaries (Y6 t1) and dictionaries of proverbs (Y6 t2) • To use a range of dictionaries and understand their purpose (Y5 t3 *W11*) • To use dictionaries efficiently to explore spellings, meanings, derivations (Y5 t3 *W12*)	• Is a dictionary just for checking spellings? • What information can you find in this dictionary? • How is the information organised in this book/page/entry?

NON-FICTION TEXT: GENERIC FEATURES

Commentary

From whose perspective is the information presented? While information books claim to convey accurate information, the author has a particular viewpoint and position. However, the apparent absence of the author from the text, the impersonal verbs and the use of 'it' rather than 'I', make it harder to detect the author's perspective. The author's perspective may be indicated more by the selection and omission of material than by its overt treatment. The omission of material may be hard to detect, especially for a learner who is unfamiliar with the field.

The predominantly white, upper-class male perspective of history texts is now recognised as biased but explained by the paucity of information about people of lower status. Many authors and publishers now try to ensure more balanced presentations.

Sometimes there are controversial topics where the author may present both sides of the argument and then explain why some evidence is more persuasive than others. More often, the author does not adopt an explicit stance but manipulates the reader more subtly through the selection of information.

How can a learner become aware of the author's perspective? Comparing texts by different authors on the same topic is a useful way to see what information has been selected, what emphasis has been given to it and from whose perspective the author is writing. Whose views are presented? Which groups of people are portrayed? Illustrations and captions may be as significant as the words for indicating perspective.

Commentary

Not all information books are reference texts, although we sometimes use these terms interchangeably. Reference texts are encyclopaedias, dictionaries, thesauruses, atlases, maps, directories, the *Guinness Book of Records*, etc.

While encyclopaedias and dictionaries will be organised alphabetically, atlases and directories will be organised in some other way. The arbitrary alphabetic organisation of the material and the limited amount of information

provided distinguish reference books from other kinds of expository text such as information books.

The overall form of reference texts will be non-narrative because narrative is not the organising principle, but there may be narrative elements within the entries. For example, in an encyclopaedia, an entry on medicine might include a narrative description of Fleming's serendipitous discovery of penicillin.

NON-FICTION TEXT: GENERIC FEATURES

Features	NLS Framework	Prompt Questions
ILLUSTRATIONS **Photographs** **Diagrams** **Charts** **Tables** **Exploded diagrams** **Line drawings**	• How written instructions are organised e.g. diagrams with arrows (Y3 t2 *T14*) • To identify the features of recounted texts such as sports reports, diaries, police reports, including supporting illustrations (Y5 t1 t21)	• What do the diagrams tell you that the words do not? • If you just look at the pictures, what would you say this book was about? • What can you find out by looking at the photographs? • Why is this exploded diagram better than a photograph?

NON-FICTION TEXT: GENERIC FEATURES

Illustrations in information text are intended to convey accurate information while in fiction they are included to heighten interpretation. Information texts frequently use photographs to emphasise realism and these are often enlarged many times, as in photographs of parts of flowers or insects or microscopic particles, with no indication of the real size of the object. While photographs produced by electron microscopes or telescopes offer us pictures of things invisible to the naked eye, these representations may still be difficult to comprehend. Photographs may be 'real' but they are not necessarily simple.

It is worth noting that in certain fields – botanical drawings, medical textbooks – drawings have long been regarded as a superior form of representation to photographs, and are valued for the ability of the artist to select and display the relevant information clearly and accurately.

While 'a picture can be worth a thousand words', it is worth looking critically at whether the illustration enhances the text, amplifies it, explains it or confuses it. Are the illustrations referred to in the text so the reader is instructed where to search for information? Although children are becoming increasingly sophisticated through their exposure to animated artwork and computer presentations, they may still have difficulty interpreting charts and diagrams correctly. Exploded diagrams may not follow the conventions of relative size and perspective – where smaller objects are further away – and may thus be confusing.

Dorling Kindersley has specialised in large-format books of detailed, exploded drawings with text alongside. Stephen Biesty's work, for example *Incredible Cross-Sections*, seems to have a strong appeal to both children and adults and the amount of detail included in his exploded drawings provides more than a functional representation. His pictures also 'tell stories' by including details that are not strictly necessary, for example the busker included in the subway station or the surprised occupant of the toilet cubicle in the car

factory. The sophistication of these diagrammatic illustrations is seductive; it is tempting to think that all you have to do is 'read the pictures'. But these pictures are often illustrating processes, and the pictures alone cannot tell the whole story. While some children may think that all they need to do is look at the pictures, this will not enable them to grasp many important features. Books like these seem to have particular appeal to boys in Key Stage 2 because they are examples of reading material which is not proficiency-graded and where the reader can draw out considerable information from the illustrations and captions, with minimal recourse to the dense text. For this reason, it might be interesting to devote at least one guided reading session to comparing the layout and information conveyed in a Dorling Kindersley book with that presented in a more conventional information book. The Empire State Building (in *Incredible Cross-Sections*) might be compared to *Towers and Bridges* by Julie Fitzpatrick (Hamish Hamilton: 1986) or *Structures* by Malcolm Dixon (Wayland: 1990).

The NLS seems to have a restricted view of what a 'text' includes, focusing primarily on linguistic features. This approach is rather narrow given the emergence of multi-media texts and the importance of photographs and other images in advertising. While the NLS lists 'to evaluate advertisements for their impact, appeal and honesty' (Y4 t3 *T19*) it follows this with 'focusing in particular on how information about the produce is presented: exaggerated claims, tactics for grabbing attention, linguistic devices, e.g. puns, jingles, alliteration, invented words.' Television and cinema advertisements rely on visual and sound effects for their impact.

The recent increase in use of the World Wide Web and other IT multi-media resources will require the development of more sophisticated means of analysing how such texts are organised and produced. Recent research has begun to examine the construction of multi-modal texts and to explore children's understanding of images and media.

REFERENCES

Chambers, A. (1993) *Tell Me*. Stroud, Gloucestershire: Thimble Press.

Littlefair, A. (1993) 'The "good book": non-narrative aspects' in R. Beard (ed.) *Teaching Literacy: Balancing perspectives*. London: Hodder and Stoughton.

Longacre, R. (1976) *An Anatomy of Speech Notions*. Liss: Peter de Riddes.

Neate, B. (1992) *Finding Out About Finding Out*. Sevenoaks: Hodder and Stoughton/ UKRA.

PART 6

Professional development opportunities

Guiding Reading: A handbook for teaching guided reading at Key Stage 2 can be used to inform and stimulate professional development. This section outlines two staff meetings (of about 1¼ hours each) focused on guided reading, which may help schools to consider their use of guided reading as a teaching strategy for children who have nearly achieved NC Level 3 or above. They are not definitive but offered as a model to be adapted to suit the school's circumstances.

The outline staff meetings are followed by some further suggestions of foci for additional staff meetings, concerning the management and organisation of guided reading in Key Stage 2 departments.

It is recommended that one member of staff (probably the Literacy Co-ordinator) prepares and organises as well as directs these INSET sessions.

AIMS OF PROFESSIONAL DEVELOPMENT SESSIONS

For participants to:

- consider the teaching objectives which are appropriate for those children in Key Stage 2 who have nearly achieved NC Level 3 and beyond;
- discuss the range of texts which could form the basis of guided reading sessions;
- understand how guided reading can provide a powerful context for the explicit and targeted teaching of reading to groups of pupils of similar ability;
- plan one or more guided reading session for a specific group of pupils in their class;
- carry out and evaluate the guided reading sessions planned;
- contribute to an action plan for the school for the further development of guided reading in Key Stage 2.

OUTLINE OF STAFF MEETING 1

BEFORE THE SESSION

1. Collect together the following resources:

   - copies of the NC levels for reading
   - copies of the *NLS Framework for teaching*
   - examples of some of the texts mentioned in *Guiding Reading: A handbook for teaching guided reading at Key Stage 2*
   - copies of one or two exemplar guided reading sessions from *Guiding Reading*, Part 4.

2. Ask staff to bring with them a text they would use for guided reading for a group in their class who are currently reading at NC Level 3 or beyond. This will be used as the basis for the planning activity. (The Literacy Co-ordinator may wish to supplement these with further examples of quality texts which the school has – see book lists in Part 4 for suggestions.)

It would be useful for staff to bring the reading records for this group detailing pupils' achievements.

INTRODUCTION (20 MINUTES)

Part 1

- INSET presenter outlines aims of INSET sessions;
- INSET presenter reminds participants of the main features of guided reading.

Part 2

Teaching objectives for pupils at NC Level 3 and beyond.

- Staff consider NC levels descriptors for Reading. What are the main areas for development and teaching for children who are at NC Level 3 and above?
- Compare NC Level 3 descriptors with NC Level 4 descriptors and consider what the differences are.
- Staff then look at NLS Framework for teaching for their year group, with the following questions to focus discussion and planning:

What specific teaching objectives from the Framework are targeted on developing pupils' reading in this way? (I.e. moving them from NC Level 3 to Level 4, or from Level 4 to Level 5.)

With a group of pupils from your own class in mind select and formulate two or three teaching objectives to focus on in future guided reading sessions for that group, based on the above and your reading assessments.

GUIDED READING AT KEY STAGE 2 (20 MINUTES)

INSET organiser:

- Draws attention to *Guiding Reading* and gives brief overview of content (see contents page for prompts).
- Distributes copies of the exemplar guided reading session selected. Participants look at sequence and structure.

Key points

- Teaching objectives are the starting point and should be clear to pupils.
- A range of quality texts is needed.
- Each guided reading session or sequence of sessions should include most, but not necessarily all, of the following elements:
    - Book introduction (by teacher and/or pupils).
    - Strategy check (where a specific reading 'searchlight' is reinforced in the context of the book chosen).
    - Independent reading by pupils.
    - Returning to the text (to reinforce key reading strategies).
    - Response to the text (to develop personal preference and extend comprehension).
    - Independent activity/further reading (to extend and reinforce the teaching objectives taught during the guided reading session).

PLANNING ACTIVITY (20–30 MINUTES)

Participants in pairs select a text and use the planner on p. 181 to plan one, or a sequence of guided reading sessions, using the exemplar as a model.

Participants should also refer to the question types on p. 27 in order to plan some strategic prompts and questions to be used during the discussion with the group and when intervening with individual pupils.

PLENARY (10 MINUTES)

- Participants outline their teaching objectives and texts to another pair/whole staff. They explain what they are going to do which is different to or extends what they have done before, as a result of this staff meeting.

FOLLOW-UP

Teachers carry out planned sessions in class and evaluate them.

GUIDED READING PLANNER

Teaching group:	
Teaching objective(s):	
Text:	
Teaching sequence: **Book introduction:**	
Strategy check:	
Independent reading (and related task):	
Returning/ responding to the text:	
Follow-up independent work/further reading:	
Evaluation and points for future teaching:	

OUTLINE OF STAFF MEETING 2

BEFORE THE SESSION

1. Remind staff to bring their plans and evaluations of the guided reading session that they completed at the last session.
2. Collect the following resources:
   - flipchart/large sheet of paper;
   - flipchart pens.

INTRODUCTION

- Remind participants about the previous meeting. Explain that they are to get together with two or three other members of staff to outline briefly what their experiences were when they taught the guided reading session planned. They should also note down key issues to be addressed if they and the school are to be able to utilise the teaching strategy of guided reading effectively.

FEEDBACK DISCUSSIONS/ PLENARY

Groups feedback key issues which are collated on the flipchart under suitable headings.

ACTION PLANNING

Staff decide what the next steps should be in terms of action. The Literacy Co-ordinator/SMT formulates a clear action plan, building on whole-staff decisions.

FURTHER SUGGESTIONS FOR PROFESSIONAL DEVELOPMENT FOR SCHOOL STAFF AND/OR INDIVIDUAL TEACHERS

1. Extending staff knowledge of Key Stage 2 texts:
   - Use the book lists included in *Guiding Reading* and collect together as many texts as possible in a central resource area so that teachers can familiarise themselves with the texts.
   - Teachers can also consider how these texts might be used in guided reading sessions in their class.

2. Organising and auditing guided reading resources for the school.

3. Reviewing and enhancing guided reading:
   - Compare the differences between guided reading and other learning experiences
   - Compare the exemplar guided reading sessions in this book with the current practice in their own classrooms/year group and adapt future teaching in the light of this analysis.

PART 7
Further reading

By this stage of the book, you may have discovered areas of interest that you would like to explore further. To help you to do this, we have drawn up some lists which are organised as follows:

BOOKS ABOUT READING AND THE TEACHING OF READING

Reading

Appleyard, J.A. (1990) *Becoming A Reader.* Cambridge: Cambridge University Press.

Bielby, N. (1999) *Teaching Reading at KS2.* Cheltenham: Stanley Thornes.

Chambers, A. (1993) *Tell Me.* Stroud, Gloucestershire: Thimble Press.

Goodwin, P. (ed.) (1999) *The Literate Classroom.* London: David Fulton.

Graham, J. (1997) *Cracking Good Books: Teaching literature at KS2.* Sheffield: NATE.

Graham, J. and Kelly, A. (eds) (1998) *Reading Under Control.* London: David Fulton.

Hall, C. and Coles, M. (1999) *Children's Reading Choices.* London: Routledge.

Marriott, S. (1995) *Using Fiction in the Primary School.* London: Paul Chapman.

Millard, E. (1997) *Differently Literate: Boys, girls and the schooling of literacy.* London: Falmer Press.

Minns, H. (1997) *Read It To Me Now* (2nd edn). Buckingham: Open University Press.

Oakhill, J. and Garnham, A. (1988) *Becoming a Skilled Reader.* Oxford: Blackwell.

Perera, K. (1984) *Children's Writing and Reading: Analysing classroom language.* Oxford: Blackwell.

Thomas, H. (1998) *Reading and Responding to Fiction: Classroom strategies for developing literacy.* Leamington Spa: Scholastic.

Children's literature

Anderson, H. and Styles, M. (2000) *Teaching Through Texts.* London: Routledge.

Carter, J. (1999) *Talking Books.* London: Routledge.

Cliff Hodges, G., Drummond, M.J. and Styles, M. (eds) (2000) *Tales, Tellers and Texts.* London: Cassell.

Cullinan, B. (1997) *Literature and the Child.* New York: Harcourt Publishers Ltd.

Egoff, S., Stubbs, G., Ashley, R. and Sutton, S. (eds) (1996) *Only Connect: Readings on children's literature* (3rd edn). Oxford: Oxford University Press.

Hunt, P. (1994) *An Introduction to Children's Literature.* Oxford: Oxford University Press.

—(2001) *Children's Literature.* Oxford: Blackwell Publishers.

Meek, M., Warlow, A. and Barton, G. (1977) *The Cool Web: The pattern of children's reading.* London: Bodley Head.

Nodelman, P. (1996) *The Pleasures of Children's Literature* (2nd edn). White Plains, NY: Longman.

Pinsent, P. (1997) *Children's Literature and the Politics of Equality.* London: David Fulton.

Reynolds, K. (1994) *Children's Literature in the 1890s and 1990s.* Plymouth: Northcote House.

Sarland, C. (1991) *Young People Reading: Culture and response.* Buckingham: Open University Press.

Styles, M., Bearne, E. and Watson, V. (1992) *After Alice.* London: Cassell.

—(1996) *Voices Off: Texts, contexts and readers.* London: Cassell.

Tucker, N. (1996) *The Child and the Book.* Cambridge: Cambridge University Press.

Book selection

Ellis, S. and Barrs, M. (1996) *The Core Book.* London: CLPE.

Irvin, N. and Cooper, L. (1999) *Who Next...?: A guide to children's authors.* Loughborough: University of Loughborough, LISU.

Lazim, A. and Ellis, S. (2000) *Choosing Texts for the National Literacy Strategy.* London: CLPE.

Powling, C. and Styles, M. (1996) *A Guide to Poetry 0–13.* Reading: University of Reading, RALIC.

Stones, R. (ed.) (1998) *Children's Books about Bullying.* Reading: University of Reading, RALIC.

Stones, R. (ed.) (1999) *A Multicultural Guide to Children's books 0–16+.* London: Books for Keeps.

DIFFERENT TYPES OF BOOKS

This section of the book list is intended to support teachers who want to engage in further research about different text types in order to support their teaching.

Myths and legends

Bearne, E. (1992) 'Myth and legend: the oldest language?' in M. Styles, E. Bearne and V. Watson, *After Alice: Exploring children's literature*. London: Cassell.

Graves, R. (1992) *Greek Myths Complete Edition*. Harmondsworth: Penguin.

Kerven, R. (2000) 'Are traditional stories sexist?' in *Books for Keeps* 122: May.

Lines, K. (ed.) (2001) *The Faber Book of Greek Legends*. London: Faber.

McCaughrean, G. and Chichester Clark, E. (2001) *Roman Myths*. New York: Simon and Schuster, Margaret McElderry Books.

Wilkins, W.J. (1989) *Hindu Mythology*. New Delhi: Atlantic Books.

Folk and fairy tales

Bettelheim, Bruno (1991) *The Uses of Enchantment*. Harmondsworth: Penguin.

Hallett, M. and Karasek, B. (1996) *Folk and Fairy Tales*. Lewiston, NY: Broadview Press.

Meyer, Rudolf (1995) *The Wisdom of Fairy Tales*. Edinburgh: Floris Books.

Opie, Iona and Peter (1980) *The Classic Fairy Tales*. Oxford: Oxford University Press.

Propp, V. (1968) *The Morphology of the Folktale*. Austin: University of Texas Press.

Tartar, M. (1993) *Off With Their Heads*. Princeton, NJ: Princeton University Press.

Whitley, D. (1996) 'Aesop for children' in M. Styles, E. Bearne and V. Watson, *Voices Off*. London: Cassell.

Zipes, Jack (1997) *Happily Ever After*. New York and London: Routledge.

—(1993) *The Trials and Tribulations of Little Red Riding Hood*. New York and London: Routledge.

Collections of traditional stories for teachers

Andersen, H.C. (1993) *The Complete Hans Christian Andersen Fairy Tales*. New York: Gramercy Books.

Buck, W., illus. S. Triest (2000) *Ramayana*. Los Angeles: University of California Press.

Erdoes, R. (ed.) (1999) *American Indian Trickster Tales*. Tucson, AZ: Treasure Chest Books.

MacDonald, G. (1996) *The Gifts of the Child Christ and Other Stories and Fairy Tales*. Grand Rapids, Michigan: Eerdmans Publishing Company.

McCaughrean, G., illus. R. Fowler (1999) *One Thousand and One Arabian Nights*. Oxford: Oxford University Press.

Owens, L. (ed.) (1993) *The Complete Brothers Grimm*. New York: Gramercy Books.

Owomoyela, O. (1997) *Yoruba Trickster Tales*. Lincoln, NE: Bison.

Philip, Neil (1989) *The Cinderella Story*. Harmondsworth: Penguin.

Sandburg, C. (1998) *Rootabaga Stories*. Bedford, MA: Applewood Books.

Simpson, M. (2000) *Mahabharata: A retelling of the great story of India*. Leamington Spa: Scholastic Press.

Wilde, O. (1994) *The Happy Prince and Other Stories*. Harmondsworth: Penguin.

Zipes, J. (1989) *Beauties, Beasts and Enchantment: Classic French fairy tales*. Harmondsworth: Penguin, Meridian.

Fantasy fiction

Attebery, B. (1996) 'Women's coming of age in fantasy' in S. Egoff, G. Stubbs, R. Ashley and S. Sutton (eds), *Only Connect*. Oxford: Oxford University Press.

Eccleshare, J. (2001) *A Study of the Harry Potter Novels*. London: Continuum.

Hunt, P. and Lenz, M. (2001) *Alternative Worlds in Fantasy Fiction*. London: Continuum.

Nodelman, P. (1996) 'Some presumptuous generalisations about fantasy' in S. Egoff, G. Stubbs, R. Ashley and S. Sutton (eds), *Only Connect*. Oxford: Oxford University Press.

Pierce, T. (1996) 'Fantasy: Why kids read it, why kids need it' in S. Egoff, G. Stubbs, R. Ashley and S. Sutton (eds), *Only Connect.* Oxford: Oxford University Press.

Science fiction

Earnshaw, B. (1983) 'Planets of awful dread' in G. Fox (1995) *Celebrating Children's Literature in Education.* London: Hodder and Stoughton.

Hughes, M. (1996) 'Science fiction as myth and metaphor' in S. Egoff, G. Stubbs, R. Ashley and S. Sutton (eds), *Only Connect.* Oxford: Oxford University Press.

Pratchett, T. (1996) 'Let there be dragons' in S. Egoff , G. Stubbs, R. Ashley and S. Sutton (eds), *Only Connect.* Oxford: Oxford University Press.

Stories with familiar settings

Tucker, N. and Gamble, N. (2001) *Family Fictions.* London: Continuum.

Stories about the past and historical fiction

Agnew, K. and Fox, G. (2001) *Children at War: From the First World War to the Gulf.* London: Continuum.

Aiken, J. (1996) 'Interpreting the past' in S. Egoff, G. Stubbs, R. Ashley and S. Sutton (eds), *Only Connect.* Oxford: Oxford University Press.

Collins, F. and Graham, J. (2001) *Historical Fiction for Children.* London: David Fulton.

Paton Walsh, J. (1994) 'Memory and writing for children especially' in M. Styles, E. Bearne and V. Watson, *The Prose and the Passion*, London: Cassell.

Short, G. (1997) 'Learning through literature: historical fiction, autobiography and the holocaust', *Children's Literature in Education* 28 (4): 179–90.

Trease, G (1972) 'The historical novelist at work' in G. Fox (ed.) (1995) *Celebrating Children's Literature in Education.* London: Hodder and Stoughton.

Time-slip stories

Hall, L. (1998) 'The pattern of dead and living: Lucy Boston and the necessity of continuity', *Children's Literature in Education* 29 (4): 51–8.

Hollindale, P. (1997) 'Children of Eyam: the dramatization of history', *Children's Literature in Education* 28 (4): 205–18.

Locherbie-Cameron, M.A.L. (1996) 'Journeys through the amulet: time travel in children's fiction', *Signal* 79 (January): 45–61.

Classic fiction

Carpenter, H. (1985) *Secret Gardens.* London: Unwin Hyman.

Lurie, A. (1990) *Not in Front of the Grown-ups.* London: Cardinal Sphere Books.

Wullschlager, J. (1995) *Inventing Wonderland.* London: Methuen.

Autobiography and autobiographical fiction

Hodgson, J. (1993) *The Search for the Self.* Sheffield: Sheffield Academic Press.

Horror

Cullingford, C. (1998) *Children's Literature and its Effects*. London: Cassell: chapter 10.

Rees, C. (1999) 'Writing horror and the horror phenomenon' in J. Carter, *Talking Books*. London: Routledge.

Reynolds, K., Brennan, G. and McCarron, K. (2001) *Frightening Fiction.* London: Continuum.

Sarland, C. (1996) 'Revenge of the teenage horrors' in M. Styles, E. Bearne and V. Watson, *Voices Off.* London: Cassell.

Adventure stories

Armstrong, J. (1995) 'In defence of adventure stories' in G. Fox (ed.) *Celebrating Children's Literature in Education.* London: Hodder and Stoughton.

Butts, D. (1992) 'The adventure story' in D. Butts (ed.) *Stories and Society.* Basingstoke, Hampshire: Macmillan.

The school story

Richards, J. (1992) 'The school story' in D. Butts (ed.) *Stories and Society.* Basingstoke, Hampshire: Macmillan.

Series fiction

Collins, F. (1999) 'Reader beware – you're in for a scare: the continuing appeal of series books' in P. Pinsent (ed.) *Pop Fiction: NCRCL Papers 5.* Roehampton: NCRCL.

Daniels, J. (1996) 'Is a series reader a serious reader?' in M. Styles, E. Bearne and V. Watson, *Voices Off.* London: Cassell.

Watson, V. (2000) *Reading Series Fiction.* London: Routledge.

Girls series website:
http://www.bookloversden.com/gseries.html

Boys series website:
http://www.bookloversden.com/bseries.html

Short stories

Gamble, N. (2001) 'Stories to live by', *Books for Keeps* 129 (July).

Hollindale, P. (2001) 'Short stories for younger readers: the neglected genre', *Books for Keeps* 128 (May).

Picture books

Baddeley, P. and Eddershaw, C. (1994) *Not So Simple Picture Books.* Stoke-on-Trent: Trentham Books.

Browne, A. (1994) 'Making picture books' in M. Styles, E. Bearne and V. Watson (eds), *The Prose and the Passion.* London: Continuum.

Cotton, P. (2000) *Picture Books Sans Frontieres.* Stoke-on-Trent: Trentham Books.

Doonan, J. (1993) *Looking at Pictures in Picture Books.* Stroud: Thimble Press.

Evans, J. (ed.) (1998) *What's In the Picture?* London: Paul Chapman.

Graham, J. *Pictures on the Page.* Sheffield: NATE.

Lewis, D. (2001) *Picturing Text.* London: Routledge.

Poetry

Carter, D. (1998) *Teaching Poetry in the Primary School.* London: Fulton.

Ellis, S. (1995) *Hands on Poetry.* London, Southwark: CLPE.

Koch, K. (1989) *Rose Where Did You Get That Red? Teaching great poetry to children.* New York: Vintage Books.

Philip, N. (1999) 'The shared moment: thoughts on children and poetry', *Signal* 88 (January): 3–15.

Styles, M. (1998) *From the Garden to the Street: Three hundred years of poetry for children.* London: Cassell.

Film and audio adaptations

Cox, R. (1996) 'Audiotaped versions of children's stories', *Children's Literature in Education* 27 (1): 23–33.

Jones, S. (2000) 'Reading the movies: learning through film' in H. Anderson and M. Styles (eds), *Teaching Through Texts.* London: Routledge.

Mackey, M. (1996) 'Strip mines in the garden: old stories, new formats, and the challenge of change', *Children's Literature in Education* 27 (1): 3–21.

Marsh, J. and Millard, E. (2000) *Literacy and Popular Culture.* London: Paul Chapman.

Wordsworth, L. (n/d) *Screening Stories.* London: Film Education.

Film and Literacy. London: Film Education.

Information and non-fiction

Littlefair, A. (1993) 'The "good book": non-narrative aspects' in R. Beard (ed.) *Teaching Literacy: Balancing perspectives*. London: Hodder and Stoughton.

Mallett, M. (1992) *Making Facts Matter: Reading non-fiction 5–11*. London: Paul Chapman.

—(1999) *Young Researchers: Informational reading and writing in the early and primary years*. London: Routledge.

Meek, M. (1996) *Information and Book Learning*. Stroud, Gloucestershire: Thimble Press.

Neate, B. (1992) *Finding Out About Finding Out*. Sevenoaks: Hodder and Stoughton/UKRA.

Wray, D. and Lewis, M. (1997) *Extending Literacy: Children reading and writing non-fiction*. London: Routledge.

Different media

Craggs, C.E. (1992) *Media Education in the Primary School*. London: Routledge.

Gamble, N. and Easingwood, N. (2001) *Literacy and ICT*. London: Continuum.

Millard, E. and Marsh, J. (2000) *Literacy and Popular Culture*. London: Paul Chapman.

Robinson, M. (1997) *Children Reading: Print and television*. London: Falmer.

Tobin, J. (2000) *Good Guys Don't Wear Hats: Children's talk about the media*. Stoke-on-Trent: Trentham.

AUTHOR STUDY

This section contains lists of additional resources and further reading for authors mentioned in the exemplars.

Janet and Allan Ahlberg

Ahlberg, A. and Wegner, F. (illus.) (1984) *Please Mrs Butler.* London: Puffin.

Ahlberg, A. and Ahlberg, J. (illus.) (1999) *The Jolly Postman.* London: Viking Children's Books.

Ahlberg, A. and Ahlberg, J. (illus.) (1999) *The Jolly Pocket Postman.* London: Viking Children's Books.

Ahlberg, A. and Ahlberg, J. (illus.) (1999) *The Jolly Christmas Postman.* London: Viking Children's Books.

Ahlberg, A. and Wegner, F. (illus.) (2001) *Friendly Matches.* London: Viking Children's Books.

Martin, D. (1989) *The Telling Line: Essays on fifteen contemporary book illustrators.* London: Julia Macrae.

Nettell, S. (1994) 'Janet and Allan Ahlberg' in *Meet the Authors and Illustrators.* Leamington Spa: Scholastic.

Sheldon, P. (1999) 'Allan Ahlberg', *Authorzone* 1: 2.

David Almond

Almond, D. (1998) *Skellig.* London: Hodder Children's Books.

Almond, D. (1999) *Kit's Wilderness.* London: Hodder Children's Books.

Almond, D. (2000) *Heaven Eye.* London: Hodder Children's Books.

Almond, D. (2001) *Secret Heart.* London: Hodder Children's Books.

Reynolds, K., Brennan, G. and McCarron, K. (2001) *Frightening Fiction.* London: Continuum.

Sheldon, P. (1999) 'David Almond', *Authorzone* 1: 4.

http://www.achuka.co.uk/dasg.htm

Angela Barrett

Barrett, A. (illus.) and Waddell, M. (1992) *The Hidden House.* London: Walker Books.

Barrett, A. (1993) *The Snow Queen.* Cambridge, MA: Candlewick Press.

Barrett, A. (illus.) and McCaughrean, G. (1994) *Orchard Book of Stories from the Ballet.* London: Orchard Books.

Barrett, A. (illus.) and Poole, J. (1999) *Joan of Arc.* London: Random House, Red Fox.

Barrett, A. (2000) *The Emperor's New Clothes.* London: Walker.

Barrett, A. (illus.) and Lewis, N. (2001) *Rocking-Horse Land.* London: Walker Books.

Doonan, J. (2000) '"Beware, beware": image, word and apprehension' in G. Cliff Hodges, M.J. Drummond and M. Styles (eds), *Tales, Tellers and Texts.* London: Cassell.

Anthony Browne

Browne, A. (1990) *Changes.* London: Walker.

Browne, A. (1991) *Gorilla.* London: Walker.

Browne, A. (1992) *The Tunnel.* London: Walker.

Browne, A. (1994) *Zoo.* London: Red Fox.

Browne, A. (1995) *Through the Magic Mirror.* London: Puffin.

Browne, A. (1996) *Piggybook.* London: Walker.

Browne, A. (2000) *Voices in the Park.* London: Picture Corgi.

Browne, A. and Evans, J. (1998) 'The role of the author/artist: an interview with Anthony Browne' in J. Evans (ed.), *What's in the Picture?* London: Paul Chapman.

Doonan, J. (1983) 'Talking pictures: a new look at Hansel and Gretel', *Signal* 42 (September): 123–31.

Doonan, J. (1989) 'Realism and surrealism in Wonderland', *Signal* 56 (January): 9–30.

Doonan, J. (2000) 'Hans Christian Andersen Award 2000 to Anthony Browne', *Signal* 92 (May): 119–25.

Nettell, S. (1994) *Meet the Authors and Illustrators.* Leamington Spa: Scholastic: 32–3.

Purdon, M. (2000) 'Drawing Lessons from Anthony Browne' in H. Anderson and M. Styles, *Teaching Through Texts.* London: Routledge.

Sheldon, P. (1999) 'Anthony Browne', *Authorzone* 1: 16.

http://www.achuka.co.uk/absg.htm

Jamila Gavin

Gavin, J. (1991) *I Want to be an Angel.* London: Mammoth.

Gavin, J. (1994) *Grandpa Chatterji.* London: Mammoth.

Gavin, J. (1996) *Grandpa's Indian Summer.* London: Mammoth.

Gavin, J. (1996) *Wormholers.* London: Mammoth.

Gavin, J. (1997) *Track of the Wind.* London: Mammoth.

Gavin, J. (1998) *Someone's Watching, Someone's Waiting.* London: Mammoth.

Gavin, J. (2000) *Coram Boy.* London: Mammoth.

Channel 4, Book Box, *Grandpa Chatterji.* Video.

Channel 4, Book Box, *Grandpa Chatterji* Teachers' Guide.

Channel 4, *What's so Good About Jamila Gavin?* Video.

Channel 4, *What's so Good About Jamila Gavin?* Programme Notes.

Channel 4, *What's so Good About Jamila Gavin?* Resource Book.

Sheldon, P. (1999) 'Jamila Gavin', *Authorzone* 1: 44.

http://www.achuka.co.uk/guests/jamilasg.htm

Susan Hill

Hill, S. (1990) *Ghost Stories.* Harlow: Longman.

Hill, S. (1992) *Friends Next Door.* London: Walker Books.

Hill, S., illus. V. Littlewood (1996) *The Glass Angels.* London: Walker Books.

Hill, S., illus. P. Howard (2000) *The Glass Angels.* London: Walker Books.

Gene Kemp

Kemp, G. (1981) *Gowie Corby Plays Chicken.* London: Puffin.

Kemp, G., narr. Karpf, E. (1986) *The Clock Tower Ghost.* Audio book. Chivers Audio.

Kemp, G. (1994) *The Turbulent Term of Tyke Tiler.* London: Puffin.

Kemp, G. (1994) *The Tamworth Pig Rides Again.* London: Puffin.

Kemp, G. (1999) *The Hairy Hands.* London: Puffin.

Kemp, G. (2000) *Bluebeard's Castle.* London: Faber Children's Books.

Kemp, G. (2000) *Charlie Lewis Plays for Time.* London: Faber Children's Books.

Nettell, S. (1994) 'Gene Kemp' in *Meet the Authors and Illustrators.* Leamington Spa: Scholastic: 76–7.

Robert Munsch

Munsch, R. (2001) *Stephanie's Ponytail.* Toronto/Vancouver: Annick Press.

Munsch, R. (2001) *The Boy in the Drawer.* Toronto/Vancouver: Annick Press.

Munsch, R. (2001) *Wait and See.* Toronto/Vancouver: Annick Press.

http://www.robertmunsch.com

Colin McNaughton

McNaughton, C. (1993) *Have You Seen Who's Just Moved in Next Door to Us?* London: Walker Books.

McNaughton, C. (1994) *Jolly Roger.* London: Walker Books.

McNaughton, C. (1994) *Who's That Banging On The Ceiling?* London: Walker Books.

McNaughton, C. (1996) *Suddenly.* London: Picture Lions.

McNaughton, C. (1997) *Here Come the Aliens.* London: Walker.

McNaughton, C. (1997) *Boo!* London: Picture Lions.

McNaughton, C. (1998) *Ooops!* London: Picture Lions.

McNaughton, C. (1999) *Goal!* London: Picture Lions.

McNaughton, C. (1999) *Wish You Were Here (and I wasn't).* London: Walker.

McNaughton, C. (2000) *Don't Step on the Crack.* London: Picture Lions.

Lewis, D. (1998) 'Oops!: Colin McNaughton and "Knowingness"', *Children's Literature in Education* 29 (2): 59–68.

McNaughton, C. (2000) 'Windows into illustration', *Books for Keeps* 121 (March).

Nettell, S. (1994) 'Colin McNaughton' in *Meet the Authors and Illustrators.* Leamington Spa: Scholastic: 86.

Sheldon, P. (1999) 'Colin McNaughton', *Authorzone* 1: 84.

www.achuka.co.uk/guests/colinmcsg.htm

Jenny Nimmo

Nimmo, J. (1989) *Emlyn's Moon.* London: Egmont, Mammoth.

Nimmo, J. (1990) *The Snow Spider.* London: Egmont, Mammoth.

Nimmo, J. (1990) *The Chestnut Soldier.* London: Egmont, Mammoth.

Nimmo, J. (1992) *Ultramarine.* London: Egmont, Mammoth.

Nimmo, J. (1995) *Griffin's Castle.* London: Egmont, Mammoth.

Nimmo, J. (1995) *The Witch's Tears.* London: Harper Collins.

Nimmo, J. (1996) *The Bronze Trumpeter.* London: Egmont, Mammoth.

Nimmo, J. (1998) *The Dragon's Child.* London: Hodder Children's Books.

Cooling, W. (1999) *An Interview with Jenny Nimmo.* London: Egmont, Mammoth.

Sheldon, P. (2000) 'Jenny Nimmo', *Authorzone* 2: 100.

Philippa Pearce

Pearce, P., illus. A. Maitland (1980) *The Battle of Bubble and Squeak.* Harmondsworth: Penguin, Puffin Books.

Pearce, P., illus. C. Voake (1994) *The Way to Sattin Shore.* Harmondsworth: Penguin, Puffin Books.

Pearce, P. (1995) *A Dog So Small.* Harmondsworth: Penguin, Puffin Books.

Pearce, P. (1996) *A Century of Children's Ghost Stories.* Oxford: Oxford University Press.

Pearce, P., illus. E. Ardizzone (1998) *Minnow on the Say.* Oxford: Oxford University Press.

Pearce, P. (2000) *Tom's Midnight Garden.* London: BBC Audio Books.

Pearce, P. (2000) *'The Rope' and Other Stories.* London: Penguin, Puffin Books.

Pearce, P., narr. J. Agutter (2000) *'The Rope' and Other Stories.* Chivers Children's Audio Books.

Sheldon, P. (1999) 'Philippa Pearce', *Authorzone* 1: 94.

Townsend, J.R. (1971) *A Sense of Story.* Harlow, Essex: Longman.

Robert Louis Stevenson

Stevenson, R.L., illus. M. Peake (1992) *Treasure Island.* London: Everyman's Library.

Stevenson, R.L., illus. R. Ingpen (1992) *Treasure Island.* London: Dragons' World.

Treasure Island: Drama script. Cheltenham: Nelson Thornes (1999).

Stevenson, R.L., narr. A. Cumming, *Treasure Island.* Penguin Children's Audio.

Bell, I. (1992) *Robert Louis Stevenson.* London: Headline Publishing.

Davies, H. (1994) *The Teller of Tales: In search of Robert Louis Stevenson.* London: Sinclair Stevenson.

Gherman, B. (1996) *Robert Louis Stevenson: Teller of tales.* New York: Atheneum Books.

McLynn, F. (1993) *Robert Louis Stevenson: A biography.* London: Hutchinson.

Styles, M. (1998) *From the Garden to the Street.* London: Cassell.

http://www.stevenson-house.co.uk

Jacqueline Wilson

Wilson, J. (1992) *The Story of Tracy Beaker.* London: Yearling Books.

Wilson, J. (1993) *The Suitcase Kid.* London: Yearling Books.

Wilson, J. (1995) *Cliffhanger.* London: Yearling Books.

Wilson, J. (1997) *Bad Girls.* London: Yearling Books.

Wilson, J. (1998) *The Lottie Project.* London: Yearling Books.

Wilson, J. (2000) *The Cat Mummy.* London: Doubleday.

Wilson, J. (2000) *The Illustrated Mum.* London: Yearling Books.

Channel 4, Book Box, *Double Act.* Video.

Channel 4, Book Box, *Double Act.* Teachers' Notes.

Channel 4, *What's So Good About Jacqueline Wilson?* Video.

Channel 4, *What's So Good About Jacqueline Wilson?* Programme Notes.

Channel 4, Book Box, *Popular Writers.*

Carey, J. (2000) A*n Interview with Jacqueline Wilson.* London: Egmont, Mammoth.

Sheldon, P. (1999) 'Jacqueline Wilson', *Authorzone* 1: 124.

Tucker, N. and Gamble, N. (2001) *Family Fictions.* London: Continuum.

http://www.achuka.co.uk/guests/jwfile.htm

Benjamin Zephaniah

Zephaniah, B. (1997) *School's Out: Poems Not for School.* Edinburgh: AK Press.

Zephaniah, B. (1997) *Funky Chickens.* Harmondsworth: Puffin.

Zephaniah, B. (1997) *Funky Turkeys.* Audio Book and Music Company Ltd.

Zephaniah, B. (2000) *Wicked World.* Harmondsworth: Puffin.

Zephaniah, B. (2000) *Wicked World.* Harmondsworth: Penguin Children's Audio.

Sheldon, P. (1999) 'Benjamin Zephaniah', *Authorzone* 1: 126.

USEFUL ADDRESSES

Authorzone is available from:
Peters Bookselling Services
120 Bromsgrove Street
Birmingham
B5 6RJ
www.peters-books.co.uk/authorzone.html

Books for Keeps is available from:
Books for Keeps
6 Brightfield Road
Lee
London
SE12 8QF
E-mail: booksforkeeps@btinternet.com

Carousel is available from:
Carousel
7 Carrs Lane
Birmingham
B4 7TG
E-mail: carousel.guide@virgin.net

Children's Literature in Education is
available from:
Subscription Department
Human Sciences Press, Inc.
233 Spring Street
New York
NY 10013-1578
Fax: 001-(212) 807 1047
www.wkap.nl/prod/j/0045-6713

Film Education resources are available
from:
Alhambra House
27-31 Charing Cross Road
London
WC2H 0AU
www.filmeducation.org

Signal is available from:
The Thimble Press
Lockwood
Station Road
Woodchester
Stroud
Gloucestershire
GL5 5EQ
Fax: 01453 878599

Channel 4 Learning catalogue is available
from:
4 Learning
PO Box 100
Warwick
CV34 6TZ
E-mail: 4Learning.sales@channel4.co.uk

Appendix
NLS Illustrative
Target Statements
for reading

ILLUSTRATIVE TARGET STATEMENTS FOR READING

This list of year-by-year statements has been drawn together from the *NLS Framework for teaching* with a particular focus on reading. The statements also take account of the stages set out in the *Progression in phonics* and the criteria for assessing reading set out in the National Curriculum assessments at Years 2 and 6. The statements illustrate the key aspects of reading that need to be addressed to raise standards. They are intended as a practical guide for head teachers and literacy co-ordinators in steering and monitoring the teaching of reading. They should be used selectively in relation to the needs and contexts of each school and in any of the following ways:

- to audit reading achievement in each year group;
- to set curricular targets for year groups and learning targets for children;
- as a steer for teachers' planning;
- to help focus teaching on the key elements of reading;
- as criteria for monitoring teaching and learning.

Although these statements summarise the objectives in the NLS *Framework* they are not a substitute for it; teachers should still plan from and teach to the *Framework* objectives.

DEFINITIONS FOR READING TARGETS

WORD RECOGNITION AND PHONIC KNOWLEDGE

- Sight reading
- Knowledge of how letters represent sounds and ability to blend
- Knowledge of how words are structured

GRAMMATICAL AWARENESS

- Language features and sentence structures in texts
- How sentences work in text
- Difference between spoken and written forms
- Recognition of punctuation and its effects
- Reading fluently with attention to punctuation

USE OF CONTEXT

- Applying knowledge of the structure and form of texts to predict ideas and events within a text
- Bringing prior knowledge to the text to aid understanding

KNOWING HOW TEXTS WORK

- Understanding of text layout, organisation and structure
- Recognising different text types and their characteristics

INTERPRETATION AND RESPONSE

Literary texts

- Understanding and interpretation of texts including the ability to infer, deduce and evaluate ideas and themes presented in texts

Non-fiction

- Applying appropriate skills to the reading of fiction, non-fiction and poetry

ATTITUDE

- The development of the children's sense of themselves as readers
- Making independent choices and developing individual tastes
- Making informed judgements about texts to use for research or to read for pleasure.

RECEPTION (YR)

WORD RECOGNITION AND PHONIC KNOWLEDGE
- Read, on sight, words for YR from appendix list 1 in the NLS *Framework* and other familiar and important words
- Blend phonemes to read CVC (consonant–vowel–consonant) words
- Use phonic knowledge to attempt unknown words

GRAMMATICAL AWARENESS
- Use knowledge of simple sentence structures and repeated patterns to make predictions and check reading

USE OF CONTEXT
- Expect written text to make sense
- Use the meaning of simple stories to support predictions

KNOWING HOW TEXTS WORK
- Identify the patterns and structures of rhyme and patterned text when retelling and reciting
- Understand, and use correctly, terms referring to conventions of print: book, cover, beginning, end, page, word, letter, line
- Track the text in the correct order – page by page, left to right, top to bottom
- Make one-to-one correspondence between written and spoken words

INTERPRETATION AND RESPONSE

Literary texts
- Understand the structure of a simple story and use when re-enacting and retelling

Non-fiction
- Locate and read significant parts of a recount and identify the main points in correct sequence

ATTITUDE
- Return to favourite books, songs, rhymes to be re-read and enjoyed.

YEAR 1 AS FOR YEAR R AND:

WORD RECOGNITION AND PHONIC KNOWLEDGE

- Read, on sight, words from appendix list 1 in the NLS *Framework* and other important and familiar words
- Blend phonemes to read words containing consonant clusters and long vowel phonemes

GRAMMATICAL AWARENESS

- Use awareness of the grammar of a sentence to help to decipher new or unfamiliar words
- Read familiar texts aloud with fluency and expression appropriate to the grammar, e.g. pausing at full stops and raising voice at questions

USE OF CONTEXT

- Use an understanding of incidents, characters and settings to make predictions
- Begin to use awareness of character and dialogue to read with expression
- Use an understanding of the structure of recounts, reports and instructions to make predictions

KNOWING HOW TEXTS WORK

- Understand difference between fiction and non-fiction, and make prediction based on title, cover, blurb, etc.
- Recognise ways to create emphasis in text, e.g. *capitalisation, bold print*
- Understand how simple diagrams and charts add information

INTERPRETATION AND RESPONSE

Literary texts

- Identify and discuss the main events or key points in a text

Non-fiction

- Relate story settings and incidents to own experience
- Compare stories, identifying common themes and characters, and contribute to discussions
- Locate specific information in the text to find answers to simple questions

ATTITUDE

- Sustain independent reading of complete texts at appropriate level
- Make choices from a selection of texts and begin to justify preferences.

YEAR 2 AS FOR YEAR 1 AND:

WORD RECOGNITION AND PHONIC KNOWLEDGE

- Read, on sight, words from appendix list 1 in the NLS *Framework* and other important and familiar words
- Recognise the full range of vowel digraphs and trigraphs
- Identify syllables in order to read polysyllabic words
- Recognise common prefixes and suffixes and regular verb endings to construct the meaning of words in context

GRAMMATICAL AWARENESS

- Read aloud with intonation and expression, taking account of the punctuation, e.g. speech marks and exclamation marks

USE OF CONTEXT

- Make predictions using experience of reading books written by the same author or based on similar themes
- Use an understanding of the structures of non-chronological reports and explanations to make predictions

KNOWING HOW TEXTS WORK

- Make comparisons between books noting similarities and differences e.g. layout, theme, characters, settings
- Understand how to use alphabetically ordered texts to retrieve information
- Gain an overall impression of a text and make predictions about content/subject of a book by skim reading and by reference to title, contents and illustrations

INTERPRETATION AND RESPONSE

- Go beyond own experience or general impression and refer to text to explain meaning

Literary texts

- Make simple inferences about thoughts and feelings and reasons for actions
- Identify key themes and discuss reasons for events in stories
- Begin to understand the effects of different words and phrases e.g. to create humour, images and atmosphere

Non-fiction

- Generate questions before reading and use knowledge of texts to help retrieve specific information
- Evaluate the usefulness of the information in a particular text for answering questions

ATTITUDE

- Make choices about which texts to read based on prior reading experience and bibliographic knowledge
- Respond to text, discussing preferences with reference to favourite characters and to books with similar themes.

YEAR 3 AS FOR YEAR 2 AND:

WORD RECOGNITION AND PHONIC KNOWLEDGE

- Recognise a range of prefixes and suffixes to construct the meanings of words in context
- Recognise the function of the apostrophe in omissions and pronounce contracted forms correctly
- Recognise the full range of consonant digraphs e.g. *kn*, *wr*, *ph*

GRAMMATICAL AWARENESS

- Read aloud with intonation and expression taking account of punctuation e.g. commas to mark pauses and grammatical boundaries
- Understand how pronouns in first-, second- and third-person forms are used in sentences and apply this to maintain understanding when reading
- Understand how dialogue is punctuated and laid out and read it with appropriate expression

USE OF CONTEXT

- Know how language is used to create effects e.g. adjectives and adverbs for description and use this knowledge to create detailed mental images
- Use bibliographic knowledge e.g. recognise how an illustration or diagram relates to accompanying text

KNOWING HOW TEXTS WORK

- Understand the differences between prose and playscripts
- Understand the features of page layout in non-fiction texts e.g. titles, subheadings, labels, diagrams and charts
- Understand how to use an index to locate specific information

INTERPRETATION AND RESPONSE

- Explore underlying themes and ideas, making clear references to text

Literary texts

- When reading aloud, show awareness and understanding of the different voices in stories
- Discuss the actions of the main characters and justify views using evidence from the text

Non-fiction

- Identify the main point and summarise orally the content of a passage or text
- Use notes to summarise the main points from a passage or text
- Evaluate the usefulness of information, e.g. follow instructions to see if they work

ATTITUDE

- Sustain silent reading to include longer, more complex texts
- Draw on knowledge of authors and the types of book they write to inform choices
- Respond to and evaluate books read making explicit reference to the text
- Read aloud confidently to an audience, e.g. a playscript, a performance poem or a favourite passage from a selected text.

YEAR 4 AS FOR YEAR 3 AND:

WORD RECOGNITION AND PHONIC KNOWLEDGE

- Use knowledge of word formation and a more extensive range of prefixes and suffixes to construct the meaning of words in context

GRAMMATICAL AWARENESS

- Read aloud with intonation and expression taking account of punctuation, e.g. commas, dashes, hyphens
- Use knowledge of how commas, connectives and full stops are used to join and separate clauses to maintain fluency and understanding when reading
- Apply knowledge of the different uses of the apostrophe to maintain understanding

USE OF CONTEXT

- Understand narrative order and chronology tracking the passing of time in stories
- Know how style and vocabulary are linked to the purpose of the text, e.g. exaggerated writing in persuasive text

KNOWING HOW TEXTS WORK

- Understand how chapters and paragraphs are used to collect, order and build up ideas
- Make use of non-fiction features, e.g. contents, to scan and assess for relevance to the intended purpose
- Identify the features of different types of text, e.g. newspaper reports, non-chronological reports, explanations, persuasion and ICT texts, and use appropriate reading strategies, e.g. scrolling through an electronic text

INTERPRETATION AND RESPONSE

Literary texts

- Identify the use of expressive, descriptive and figurative language in prose and poetry and interpret the effect of the choice of language to create mood, build tension, etc.
- Respond critically to issues raised in stories, locating evidence in the text, exploring alternative courses of action and evaluating the author's solution

Non-fiction

- Prepare for factual research by evaluating what is known and locating relevant sources to use
- Evaluate specific texts with reference to their type, e.g. 'is an advert successful at persuading?'
- Distinguish between fact and opinion and recognise the point of view being presented in a text

ATTITUDE

- Develop different reading styles for different text types e.g. sustained silent reading for longer fiction and close reading for non-fiction
- Describe and review own reading habits
- Take part in peer-group discussion on books.

YEAR 5 AS FOR YEAR 4 AND:

WORD RECOGNITION AND PHONIC KNOWLEDGE

- Use knowledge of words, roots, derivations and spelling patterns to read unknown words
- Know how to work out the pronunciation of homophones using the context of the sentence

GRAMMATICAL AWARENESS

- In longer texts, maintain understanding by applying knowledge of the use of pronouns within sentences and between paragraphs.
- Understand how complex sentences are constructed and punctuated and use this to deepen understanding when reading

USE OF CONTEXT

- Understand how stories may vary, e.g. in pace, build up, sequence, complication and resolution
- Use knowledge of fiction and non-fiction texts to make and confirm predictions of either structure or content whilst reading

KNOWING HOW TEXTS WORK

- Identify features of different fiction genres, e.g. science fiction, adventure, myths, legends
- Know structures and grammatical features of a range of non-fiction text types, e.g. explanations, recounts, persuasive texts
- Make use of features that enable the reader to locate specific information e.g. contents, sections, headings

INTERPRETATION AND RESPONSE

Literary texts

- Identify the point of view from which a story is told and respond, e.g. by retelling from a different point of view
- Understand the differences between literal and figurative language, e.g. by discussing the effects of imagery in poetry and prose
- Recognise how characters are presented in different ways and respond to this with reference to the text
- Infer meaning with reference to text but also applying wider experience, e.g. why a character is behaving in a particular way

Non-fiction

- Locate information confidently and efficiently by using appropriate skills, e.g. skimming, scanning, text-marking, using ICT resources
- Evaluate texts critically by comparing how different sources treat the same information

ATTITUDE

- Develop an active response to own reading e.g. by empathising with characters, imagining events
- Use the blurb, front cover, reviews, etc. to make informed decisions about which books to read
- Take part in peer group discussions and be prepared to widen reading experience based on recommendation.

YEAR 6 AS FOR YEAR 5 AND:

WORD RECOGNITION AND PHONIC KNOWLEDGE

- Use knowledge of word derivations and word formation, e.g. prefixes, acronyms and letter omission, to construct the meaning of words in context

GRAMMATICAL AWARENESS

- Apply grammatical knowledge when re-reading complex sentences with appropriate phrasing and intonation
- Read fluently, understanding and using more sophisticated punctuation marks, e.g. colon, semi-colon, parenthetic commas, dashes, brackets
- Understand the use of connectives as signposts to indicate a change of tone, voice or opinion and apply this to maintain understanding when reading specific types of text

USE OF CONTEXT

- Identify the correct language conventions and features of different text types to sustain understanding when reading extended texts or from a range of sources

KNOWING HOW TEXTS WORK

- Identify and describe the styles of individual writers and poets
- Use secure understanding of the language features and structures of the full range of non-fiction text types to support understanding when reading

INTERPRETATION AND RESPONSE

- Distinguish between implicit and explicit points of view
- Comment on the success of texts and writers in evoking particular responses in the reader

Literary texts

- Analyse how messages, moods, feelings and attitudes are conveyed in poetry and prose using inference and deduction and making reference to the text
- Comment critically on the overall impact of poetry or prose with reference to a range of features, e.g. use of language, development of themes

Non-fiction

- Secure the skills of skimming, scanning and efficient reading so that research is fast and effective
- Appraise a text quickly and effectively and evaluate its value

ATTITUDE

- Declare and justify personal preferences for writers and types of text
- Decide on the quality/usefulness of a text by skim reading ...
  impression using bibliographic ...
- Articulate personal responses to ...
  the reader.

SUMMARY OF THE RANGE OF WORK FOR EACH TERM

YEAR R	EACH TERM		
Fiction and poetry	• A wide variety of traditional, nursery and modern rhymes, chants, action verses, poetry and stories with predictable structures and patterned language		
Non-fiction	• Simple non-fiction texts, including recounts		

YEAR 1	TERM 1	TERM 2	TERM 3
Fiction and poetry	• stories with familiar settings • stories and rhymes with predictable and repetitive patterns	• traditional stories and rhymes • fairy stories • stories and poems with familiar, predictable and patterned language from a range of cultures, including playground chants, action verses and rhymes • plays	• stories about fantasy worlds • poems with patterned and predictable structures • a variety of poems on similar themes
Non-fiction	• signs, labels, captions, lists, instructions	• information texts, including non-chronological reports • simple dictionaries	• information texts including recounts of observations, visits, events

YEAR 2	TERM 1	TERM 2	TERM 3
Fiction and poetry	• stories and a variety of poems with familiar settings	• traditional stories; stories and poems from other cultures • stories and poems with predictable and patterned language • poems by significant children's poets	• extended stories • stories by significant children's authors • different stories by the same author • texts with language play, e.g. riddles, tongue-twisters, humorous verse and stories
Non-fiction	• instructions	• dictionaries, glossaries, indexes and other alphabetically ordered texts • explanations	• information texts including non-chronological reports

YEAR 3	TERM 1	TERM 2	TERM 3
Fiction and poetry	• stories with familiar settings • plays • poems based on observation and the senses • shape poems	• myths, legends, fables, parables • traditional stories; stories with related themes • oral and performance poetry from different cultures	• adventure and mystery stories • stories by the same author • humorous poetry and poetry that plays with language, word puzzles, puns, riddles
Non-fiction	• information texts on topics of interest • non-chronological reports • thesauruses, dictionaries	• instructions • dictionaries without illustrations, thesauruses	• letters written for a range of purposes: to recount, explain, enquire, congratulate, complain • alphabetical texts, directories, encyclopaedias, indexes

YEAR 4	TERM 1	TERM 2	TERM 3
Fiction and poetry	• historical stories and short novels • playscripts • poems based on common themes, e.g. space, school, animals, families, feelings, viewpoints	• stories/novels about imagined worlds: sci-fi, fantasy adventures • stories in series • classic and modern poetry, including poems from different cultures and times	• stories/short novels, etc. that raise issues, e.g. bullying, bereavement, injustice • stories by same author • stories from other cultures • range of poetry in different forms, e.g. haiku, cinquain, couplets, lists, thin poems, alphabets, conversations, monologues, syllabics, prayers, epitaphs, songs, rhyming forms and free verse
Non-fiction	• a range of text types from reports and articles in newspapers and magazines • instructions	• information texts on same or similar themes • explanations	• persuasive writing: adverts, circulars, flyers • discussion texts: debates, editorials • information texts linked to other curricular areas

YEAR 5	TERM 1	TERM 2	TERM 3
Fiction and poetry	• novels, stories and poems by significant children's writers • playscripts • concrete poetry	• traditional stories, myths, legends, fables from a range of cultures • longer classic poetry, including narrative poetry	• novels, stories and poems from a variety of cultures and traditions • choral and performance poetry
Non-fiction	• recounts of events, activities, visits; observational records, news reports • instructional texts: rules, recipes, directions, instructions, showing how things are done	• non-chronological reports (i.e. to describe and classify) • explanations (processes, systems, operations, etc.). Use content from other subjects, e.g. how the digestive system works, how to find a percentage, the rain cycle	• persuasive writing to put or argue a point of view: letters, commentaries, leaflets to persuade, criticise, protest, support, object, complain • dictionaries, thesauruses, including IT sources

YEAR 6	TERM 1	TERM 2	TERM 3
Fiction and poetry	• classic fiction, poetry and drama by long-established authors including, where appropriate, study of a Shakespeare play • adaptations of classics on film/TV	• longer established stories and novels selected from more than one genre, e.g. mystery, humour, sci-fi, historical, fantasy worlds • range of poetic forms, e.g. kennings, limericks, riddles, cinquain, tanka, poems written in other forms (as adverts, letters, diary entries, conversations), free verse, nonsense verse	• comparison of work by significant children's author(s) and poets: (a) by same author (b) different authors' treatment of same theme(s)
Non-fiction	• autobiography and biography, diaries, journals, letters, anecdotes, records of observations, etc. which recount experiences and events, journalistic writing, non-chronological reports	• discussion texts • formal writing: notices, public information documents, etc.	• explanations linked to work from other subjects • non-chronological reports linked to work from other subjects • use of reference texts, range of dictionaries, thesauruses, including IT sources

Copyright acknowledgements

COPYRIGHT ACKNOWLEDGEMENTS

Annick Press	*The Paper Bag Princess* by Robert Munsch, art by Michael Martchenko (1980). Reproduced by permission of Annick Press Ltd.
Alice Bold	'The Malfeasance' by Alan Bold. Reproduced by kind permission of Alice Bold. Copyright © Alan Bold to Alice Bold.
BBC Books	Delia Smith (1998) *Delia's How to Cook (Book One).*
Birmingham Museum & Art Gallery	David Evans (1990) *How We Used to Live: Victorians Early and Late* (A&C Black in association with Yorkshire Television). Front cover features a detail from Charles Rossiter's 'To Brighton & Back for 3/6'. Reproduced by courtesy of Birmingham Museums and Art Gallery.
B.L. Kearley Ltd	Alfred Noyes; illustrated by Charles Keeping (1981) *The Highwayman*. Text © Alfred Noyes 1913, renewed 1941. Illustrations © Charles Keeping 1981. Front cover and additional illustration reproduced by kind permission of B.L. Kearley Ltd.
Crown Copyright	*The Highway Code.* © Crown copyright.
D. C. Thomson & Co. Ltd.	Front cover and Dandy Club advertisement – featured in *The Dandy* Issue No. 3078 (November 18th 2000) Reproduced by permission of D.C. Thomson & Co. Ltd.
Egmont Children's Books Ltd	Jenny Nimmo (2001) *Milo's Wolves*. Cover Illustration © 2001 Jacey. First published 2001 by Mammoth, an imprint of Egmont Books Limited. Used with permission.
Evans Brothers Limited	*Focus on Pakistan*. Copyright © Mano Rumalshah 1989. Published by Evans Brothers Limited, 2A Portman Mansions, Chiltern Street, London W1U 6NR.
HarperCollins Publishers Ltd.	Jacket illustration from *Centuries of Stories* edited by Wendy Cooling. Jacket illustration copyright © Matilda Harrison. Reproduced by permission of HarperCollins Publishers Ltd.
Hodder Children's Books	Jamila Gavin (1997) *Out of India: an Anglo-Indian Childhood*. Hodder Children's Books.
Hodder Wayland	Reproduced by permission of Hodder Wayland:
	Sue Crawford, illus. John Haysom (1998) *A Family in the Thirties*.
	Christa Stadder (1991) *The United Kingdom*.
	Richard Wood (1994) *Family Life in Victorian Britain*.
Jonathon Clowes	'The Owl' by David Harsent. Copyright © 1996 David Harsent. Reprinted by kind permission of Jonathan Clowes Ltd., London, on behalf of David Harsent.